Take Charge of Your Health!

Self-Assessment Workbook with Review and Practice Tests

Health: The Basics

SIXTH EDITION

Rebecca J. Donatelle

Prepared by

Lynne Blesz Vestal

PEARSON

Benjamin Cummings

San Francisco   Boston   New York
Cape Town   Hong Kong   London   Madrid   Mexico City
Montreal   Munich   Paris   Singapore   Sydney   Tokyo   Toronto

Publisher: Daryl Fox
Development Manager: Claire Alexander
Acquisitions Editor: Deirdre McGill Espinoza
Project Editor: Susan Malloy
Assistant Editor: Christina Pierson
Director of Media Development and Publishing Technology: Lauren Fogel
Managing Editor: Deborah Cogan
Manufacturing Buyer: Stacey Weinberger
Marketing Manager: Sandra Lindelof

ISBN 0-8053-6038-7

PEARSON
Benjamin
Cummings

1 2 3 4 5 6 7 8 9 10 TCS 06 05 04
www.aw-bc.com

Contents

Promoting Healthy Behavior Change

Chapter Overview

Health is a multidimensional concept. To be truly healthy, a person must be capable of functioning at an optimal level in the physical, social, mental, environmental, spiritual, emotional, and intellectual dimensions of life. Although mortality and morbidity rates indicate that people are now living longer and are less susceptible to infectious diseases that plagued previous generations, people are not necessarily healthier. In fact, over half of Americans are overweight and unfit, and there are epidemic rates of obesity, diabetes, and other lifestyle-related maladies. A holistic approach to wellness, which emphasizes the integration of and balance among mind, body, and spirit, is believed to help individuals consider all aspects of life that can affect health. Achieving wellness means attaining the optimal level of wellness for a person's unique limitations and strengths.

Healthy People 2010 objectives aim to eliminate health disparities and increase life span and the quality of life by focusing on nutrition, tobacco use, substance abuse, access to health services, and common health conditions. Many agencies have committed themselves to achieving these objectives by developing health promotion programs aimed at reducing negative health behaviors and increasing positive behavior change at the primary, secondary, and tertiary levels. Some of the greatest public health achievements have been vaccinations, motor vehicle safety, workplace safety, control of infectious diseases, heart disease, strokes, food safety, maternal and infant care, family planning, fluoridated water, and acknowledgment that tobacco is harmful.

Gender differences are important when evaluating health status, determining the effects of certain drugs, and understanding differences in the health behaviors of men and women. Women's health issues have received more attention since the 1990s. Interest in women's health developed after 1990, when a highly publicized government study cited uneven numbers of women included in clinical research trials conducted by the National Institutes of Health (NIH). Now, both genders receive attention during clinical drug trials and by governing agencies, health care providers and others engaged in prevention, screening and treatment.

Individual behavior is a major determinant of good health. Other factors influencing an individual's health status include interpersonal, social, and work influences; community influences; heredity; access to health care; and the environment. There are many behaviors that help us to live longer with less sickness and disability, but adopting these behaviors can be difficult.

Changing negative behaviors into positive behaviors takes time and often occurs in stages. An important factor is readiness to change. Beliefs, attitudes, intentions, and the role of significant others all help to explain why we engage in healthy or unhealthy behaviors. Predisposing, reinforcing, and enabling factors are useful guides for analyzing behavior and planning strategies for change.

Strategies for change include shaping, visualization, modeling, changing situations to control behaviors, reinforcement, and changing self-talk. When changing behaviors, record your behavior and analyze antecedents and consequences that reinforce the behavior and obstacles to success. Behavior change requires commitment, realistic goals, and the help of people who truly care about you.

NAME: _____ DATE: _____

TAKE CHARGE WORKSHEET 1.1

Health Behavior Self-Assessment

DIRECTIONS: Answer the following questions about your health and behavior. After answering these questions, use the information to write a narrative description about yourself and your health risks.

Family Health History

Check any health problems that your parents or biological siblings have had.

✓ Allergies	_____ Alcoholism	M_____ Asthma	_____ Angina
_____ Breast cancer	_____ Colon cancer	_____ Lung cancer	_____ Ovarian cancer
_____ Prostate cancer	_____ Skin cancer	_____ Testicular cancer	_____ Other cancer
✓ Diabetes	✓ Emphysema	_____ Endometriosis	_____ Fibromyalgia
_____ Gout	M ✓ High blood pressure	✓ High cholesterol	_____ HIV
_____ Cystic fibrosis	✓ Heart disease	✓ Pneumonia	_____ Tuberculosis
_____ Multiple sclerosis	_____ Mononeucleosis	_____ Leukemia	_____ Rheumatoid arthritis
_____ Sickle cell anemia	_____ Alzheimer's disease	_____ Neurological disorder	

Other: _____

Personal Health History

1. List any chronic health problems you have.

2. List any surgeries you have had.

3. List any disabilities you have.

4. List any medications you take on a regular basis.

5. List any allergies you have.

General Health

Age: _____   Height: _____   Resting heart rate: _____

Gender: _____   Current weight: _____   Blood pressure: _____

Calculate your ideal body weight by using the following formula:

For females, add 100 lb for the first 5 feet in height and 6 lb per inch after that.

For males, add 125 lb for the first 5 feet in height and 6 lb per inch after that.

My ideal body weight is: _____.

Subtract 5 lb if you are small framed; add 5 lb if you are large framed.

To measure frame size, grasp your wrist around the wrist bones with your thumb and forefinger. If your thumb and forefinger overlap, you are small framed. If your thumb and forefinger touch, you are medium framed. If your thumb and forefinger do not touch, you are large framed.

According to this formula,

I am _____ lbs. overweight.

I am _____ lbs. underweight.

Sleep Assessment

1. How many hours of sleep per night do you get?

2. What time do you go to bed?

3. What time do you normally get up?

4. Do you have a regular sleep/wake schedule?

5. Do you take naps?

6. Are you sleepy during the day?

7. Have you ever fallen asleep in class, at work, or while driving?

Fitness Assessment

1. How many hours of television do you watch per day?

2. Do you have any back, hip, knee, or ankle problems?

3. Do you have any neck, shoulder, elbow, wrist, or writing problems?

4. Do you have any respiratory or heart problems?

5. How far past your toes can you reach with your fingertips (knees straight)?

6. How many sit-ups can you do in one minute (knees bent, hands behind head, touching elbows to knees)?

7. How many push-ups can you do in one minute?

8. Can you jog or run continuously for 20 minutes?

9. What is your favorite type of exercise?

10. What is your favorite sport to play?

Nutritional Assessment

1. Do you eat breakfast?

2. Are you lactose intolerant?

3. Do you have any food allergies?

4. How many servings of dairy do you consumer per day (8 oz. of milk, 1.5 oz of cheese, 1 cup of ice cream, 1 cup of yogurt, 1 cup of cottage cheese)?

5. How many servings of fruits and vegetables do you consume per day ($1/2$ cup of raw or cooked, 1 cup of lettuce)?

6. How many servings of meat do you consume per day (3 oz., the size of a deck of cards or a floppy disk)?

7. How many servings of grains/cereals do you consume per day (1 slice of bread, 1 cup of rice or pasta)?

8. How many soft drinks do you consume per day?

9. How many snacks do you have during the day?

10. Do you take a multivitamin or any type of food supplement? What kind?

11. How often do you drink protein drinks?

Stress Assessment

1. In general, are you optimistic or pessimistic about life?

2. Do you feel good about yourself most of the time?

3. In general, do you feel that you have control over most things in your life?

4. Do you have more things to do than you have time to do them?

5. Do you worry about things?

6. Are you anxious about things that you can not control in your life?

7. Do you often hear yourself saying negative things to yourself?

8. Do you have a few close friends that you can count on?

9. Do you have trouble paying your bills?

10. Do you allow enough time to study each day?

11. Do you have difficulties with parents, teachers, friends, or roommates?

Emotional Assessment

1. Do you feel that you make good decisions?

2. If there is a problem, are you able to speak to the person about it?

3. Do you solve problems or allow them to continue?

4. Do you have difficulty getting to sleep and staying asleep at night?

5. Do you frequently feel angry?

6. Have you felt sad or depressed for more than two weeks?

7. Have you lost interest in school or in things your friends are doing?

8. Have you had a significant life change recently?

9. Have you suffered any personal losses within the past year?

10. Do you eat, smoke, or drink alcohol in order to relax?

11. Do you have any unusual fears that you cannot explain?

Substance Use Assessment

1. How much caffeine (chocolate, tea, coffee, other stimulants) do you use per day?

2. How many cigarettes do you smoke per day?

3. How much smokeless tobacco do you use per day?

4. How many alcoholic drinks do you consume on an average day?

5. How many alcoholic drinks do you consume when you go out with friends?

6. How often do you go out with friends?

7. How often do you take prescription medication?

8. Do you take prescription medication as directed, more often, higher doses, etc.?

9. Have you tried any other stimulants such as Ephedra, ecstasy, cocaine, or crack?

10. Have you tried or do you use marijuana? How often?

11. Have you tried or do you use hallucinogens such as GHB, mushrooms, peyote, or LSD?

12. Have you tried or do you use narcotics such as morphine, heroin, or Oxycotin?

Driving Assessment

1. How many miles do you drive per week?

2. How many traffic tickets have you had?

3. How many accidents have you had?

4. Do you obey traffic signs and signals?

5. How often do you exceed the speed limit?

6. Do you wear your seat belt or helmet?

7. Do you get upset with other drivers and act on impulses?

8. Have you ever been in an argument or a fight with another driver?

9. Have you ever driven while drunk?

10. Do you ride with other drivers who have been drinking?

Sexual Health Assessment

1. Are you able to practice abstinence?

2. Are you confident in discussing sexual issues with a prospective partner?

3. If you are sexually active, do you use a condom to prevent sexually transmitted diseases or pregnancy?

4. Have you ever had a sexually transmitted disease?

5. Have you been the victim of rape?

6. In the past year, have you had more than one sexual partner?

7. Females: Do you have a pelvic exam each year?

8. Have you ever had an HIV test?

Preventive Health Behaviors Assessment

1. Do you have your eyes checked each year?

2. Do you brush and floss your teeth daily?

3. Do you visit your dentist once a year to check for cavities and to have your teeth cleaned?

4. Do you examine your breasts or scrotum each month for lumps?

5. Do you use sunscreen protection? Have you used tanning beds?

6. Have you had a tuberculosis test recently?

7. Do you wash your hands after using the bathroom and before eating?

8. Do you walk or travel with a friend at night?

9. Do you lock your car and your home to prevent crimes?

10. Do you have a fire detector in your home?

Your Health Risks

Use the information gathered from the questions above to write a paragraph describing you and your health risks.

EVALUATION: We often develop habits because we are not thinking about what we do. Now that you have finished the assessment, do you see some areas in your lifestyle or your habits that need some changing or adjustment? What are the top three things you might want to change? Are they important to you? Are you ready to change? Do you think your family, friends, and roommates would be supportive of your change? What type of obstacles do you think you might encounter? What would you have to do to overcome the obstacles? How successful do you think you might be?

Now, select the *one* habit that will have the most profound impact on your health and that you are certain you can change. It is important to start with a behavior that we are confident we can change. After that habit has been changed, you may be inspired to change others. Let your friends know about the changes you plan to make. Instead of making it difficult for you, you may be helping them change too!

NAME: _____ DATE: _____

TAKE CHARGE WORKSHEET 1.2

Behavior Change Project

PURPOSE: To help you apply self-management strategies to improve a health behavior.

DIRECTIONS: Follow the steps below to help you choose and change a behavior to improve your health.

Step 1: Complete the *How Healthy Are You?* assessment in your textbook (pages 6–10), Take Charge Worksheet 1.1: *Health Behavior Self-Assessment,* or an on-line health-risk assessment such as those found on the web site: www.youfirst.com. Determine which dimension (physical, social, emotional, environmental, spiritual, or intellectual) needs improvement. Review your answers to the questions and determine which health behavior is the most changeable and most important to improve your current health status.

Step 2: Complete Take Charge Worksheet 1.3: *Behavior Change Agreement* to plan, monitor, and evaluate your progress toward changing a specific behavior. Make sure that someone interested in your health signs the contract and helps you monitor your progress each week.

Step 3: Keep a journal Sunday through Saturday, writing down the frequency and other factors of the behavior that are important.

EXAMPLES: If you want to get more sleep at a regular time, write down the time you go to bed, how many times during the night you wake up, the time you woke up, how long it took you to get out of bed in the morning, whether you felt sleepy during the day, and whether you thought you needed a nap. If you want to eat healthier, write down the foods you are eating, the portion sizes, time of day, and include beverages.

If you want to exercise more, write down the frequency, intensity, duration, and type of exercise, and time of day. If you want to decrease the amount of caffeine, nicotine, or alcohol you use each day, write down the time of day, type of substance, amount, and anything that might have "triggered" the urge to use the substance.

Step 4: At the end of each week, use Take Charge Worksheet 1.4: *Weekly Behavior Change Evaluation* as a guide to evaluate your success throughout the project. If there are problems, identify them and develop strategies to improve success.

Step 5: Do this project for at least 4–6 weeks or until you achieve your goal.

NAME: _____ DATE: _____

TAKE CHARGE WORKSHEET 1.3

Behavior Change Agreement

DIRECTIONS: Complete this Behavior Change Agreement or your text's Behavior Change Contract to plan, monitor, and evaluate your progress toward changing a specific behavior. A sample agreement is on the next page.

Personal Information

Age: _____   Height: _____   Resting heart rate: _____

Gender: _____   Weight: _____   Blood pressure: _____

Self-Assessment Results

According to the *Health Behavior Self-Assessment,* I need to improve:

Behavior Change Goals

The goal I hope to achieve in 4–6 weeks is _____

_____

Obstacles I expect to encounter during this project include _____

_____

I can improve my chances for success on this project if I _____

_____

My goal for the first week of this project is to _____

_____

Rewards

If I achieve my goal each week, I will reward myself by _____

_____

_____   _____
Signature   Witness Signature

_____   _____
E-mail or Phone Number   E-mail or Phone Number

_____   _____
Date   Date

_____   _____
Instructor Signature   Date

Sample Behavior Change Agreement

Personal Information

Age: 20 years

Gender: Female

Height: 5'5"

Weight: 145 lb

Resting heart rate: 72 bpm

Blood pressure: 120/80

Self-Assessment Results

According to the self-assessment, I need to *improve my weight. According to the height/weight tables, I need to lose approximately 10–15 lb to improve my health. I could do this if I eat more fruits, vegetables, and grains and less sugar and fat. I could also add daily aerobic exercise to lose approximately 1–2 lb per week.*

Behavior Change Goals

The goal I hope to achieve in 4–6 weeks is to *lose 8–10 lb by eating more fruits, vegetables, and grains and exercising daily.*

Obstacles I expect to encounter during this project include *the tendency to eat snack foods, convenience foods, and fast food.*

I can improve my chances for success on this project if I *stop buying snack foods, convenience foods, and fast food every day. I could also go to the grocery store each week and buy fruits, juices, vegetables, and grains I like that I could carry in my backpack when I get hungry.*

My goal for the first week of this project is to *eat 3–5 fruits and vegetables per day.*

Rewards

If I achieve my goal each week, I will reward myself by *eating a favorite dessert, snack, or other food that I enjoy on the weekend.*

Note: Rewards can be tangible (money, purchased item, free time, self-indulgence, a long-distance telephone call to a friend or relative, etc) or social (praise, approval, acceptance, acknowledgement, recognition).

Signature

E-mail or Phone Number

Date

Instructor Signature

Witness Signature

E-mail or Phone Number

Date

Date

NAME: _____ DATE: _____

TAKE CHARGE WORKSHEET 1.4

Weekly Behavior Change Evaluation

DIRECTIONS: Answer the following questions for each week of your behavior change project and for the final evaluation of the entire project.

1. What was your goal for this behavior change project?

2. What was your goal for the week?

3. Did you keep a journal of your behavior?

4. What did your journal reveal about your behavior?

5. What other observations did your partner or instructor see in your journal?

6. Did you achieve your weekly goal? Did you give yourself a reward for success?

7. What contributed to your success or failure?

8. What goal will you set for next week?

9. How will you reward yourself next week?

10. What are you learning about yourself with this self-management project?

TAKE CHARGE WORKSHEET 1.5

Outline for Self-Assessment Writing Assignment

DIRECTIONS: Write a paragraph under each of the headings below. An example is provided below. You may use your responses for Take Charge Worksheet 1.1 to help you write your paragraphs.

Sample Description of Self

Andy is an 18-year-old Caucasian male enrolled as a freshman in college. His typical day consists of going to classes Monday, Wednesday, and Friday mornings and working in the afternoons. Tuesday and Thursday are free days used to study and work out in the gym. Andy lives in the dorms and his family lives several hours away. He attends church services each Sunday and spends time with friends on the weekends. He would like to be a junior high school teacher one day.

Description of Self

Family Health History

Personal Health History

General Health

Sleep Assessment

Fitness Assessment

Nutritional Assessment

Stress Assessment

Emotional Assessment

Substance Use Assessment

Driving Assessment

Sexual Health Assessment

Preventive Health Behaviors Assessment

NAME: _____ DATE: _____

TAKE CHARGE WORKSHEET 1.6

Multidimensional Health Locus of Control

DIRECTIONS: Indicate your degree of agreement with each of the following statements by placing a number in the blank before it. Use the following scale:

5 = strongly agree

4 = agree

3 = neither agree nor disagree

2 = disagree

1 = strongly disagree

Subscale A: Internal

_____ 1. If I get sick, it is my own behavior that determines how soon I get well.

_____ 2. I am in control of my health.

_____ 3. When I get sick, I am to blame.

_____ 4. The main thing that affects my health is what I myself do.

_____ 5. If I take care of myself, I can avoid illness.

_____ 6. If I take the right actions, I can stay healthy.

Subscale B: Powerful Others

_____ 1. Having regular contact with my physician is the best way for me to avoid illness.

_____ 2. Whenever I don't feel well, I should consult a medically-trained professional.

_____ 3. My family has a lot to do with my becoming sick or staying healthy.

_____ 4. Health professionals control my health.

_____ 5. When I recover from an illness, it's usually because other people (e.g., doctors, nurses, family, and friends) have been taking good care of me.

_____ 6. Regarding my health, I can do only what my doctor tells me to do.

Subscale C: Chance

_____ 1. No matter what I do, if I am going to get sick, I will get sick.

_____ 2. Most things that affect my health happen to me by accident.

_____ 3. Luck plays a big part in determining how soon I will recover from an illness.

_____ 4. My good health is largely a matter of good fortune.

_____ 5. No matter what I do, I'm likely to get sick.

_____ 6. If it's meant to be, I will stay healthy,

EVALUATION: To obtain your score for a subscale, add the numbers you chose in that subscale.

1. A score of 23–30 means on any subscale means you have a strong inclination to that particular dimension. For example, a high C score indicates that you hold strong beliefs that your health is a matter of chance.

2. A score of 15–22 means that you are moderate on that particular dimension. For example, a moderate B score indicates that you have a moderate belief that your health is due to powerful others.

3. A score of 6–14 means you are low on that particular dimension. For example, a low A score means that you generally do not believe that you personally control your health.

General Review Questions

1. Distinguish between mortality and morbidity.

2. It is well known that individual behavior is a major determinant of good health. But health status can also be affected by other factors. Identify and provide examples of such factors that influence health status.

3. What are the greatest public health achievements of the twentieth century?

4. Discuss the importance of significant others as change agents.

5. What are the major behavior-change techniques?

Practice Test 1

1. The fact that people are now living longer than at any other time in history refers to what type of statistic?

   a. morbidity
   b. mortality
   c. incidence
   d. prevalence

2. What is the term for statistics used to measure death rates?

   a. morbidity
   b. mortality
   c. incidence
   d. prevalence

3. Bob and Sarah are comfortable expressing their feelings to each other, and they trust each other. This relates to what component of health?

   a. social
   b. physical
   c. spiritual
   d. intellectual

4. The performance of everyday tasks, such as bathing or walking up the stairs, is called:

   a. improved quality of life.
   b. physical health.
   c. health promotion behaviors.
   d. activities of daily living.

5. Your appraisal of the relationship between exercise and the idea that it contributes to your physical health is called a(n):

   a. attitude.

   b. cue to action.

   c. predisposing factor.

   d. belief.

6. Life experiences, knowledge, cultural and ethnic heritage, and current beliefs and values are called _____ factors influencing behavior change.

   a. predisposing

   b. enabling

   c. readiness

   d. reinforcing

7. Using the nicotine patch to help quit smoking is an example of:

   a. primary prevention.

   b. health promotion.

   c. secondary prevention.

   d. tertiary prevention.

8. What statistic is used to describe the number of existing cases of breast cancer?

   a. morbidity

   b. mortality

   c. incidence

   d. prevalence

9. Because Ann's fitness center is just across the street from her home, she exercises regularly. This illustrates which factor influencing behavior?

   a. enabling

   b. endorsing

   c. predisposing

   d. reinforcing

10. After Jill was hospitalized for dehydration and was diagnosed with anorexia nervosa, she began an inpatient treatment program designed to treat individuals with eating disorders. What type of disease prevention is she receiving?

    a. primary prevention

    b. secondary prevention

    c. tertiary prevention

    d. disease prevention

11. Practicing safe sex is an example of:

    a. primary prevention.

    b. secondary prevention.

    c. tertiary prevention.

    d. disease prevention.

12. What term refers to the state of being that precedes a behavioral change?

    a. cue to action

    b. readiness

    c. attitude

    d. locus of control

13. Suppose you want to lose 20 pounds. To reach your goal, you take small steps to gradually lose weight. You start by joining a support group and counting calories. After two weeks, you begin an exercise program and gradually build up to your desired fitness level. What behavior-change strategy are you using?

    a. shaping

    b. visualization

    c. modeling

    d. reinforcement

14. When Mary began a program to lose 40 pounds, she worked with a personal trainer. Since she had not exercised before, she gradually built up to her desired fitness level and slowly changed her eating habits, keeping her steps small and achievable. By setting weekly goals with her trainer and not skipping steps, she was able to meet her weight-loss goal. What behavior-change strategy did Mary use to lose weight?

a. shaping

b. modeling

c. visualization

d. controlling the situation

15. Albert Ellis is associated with what self-talk procedure?

a. blocking

b. thought stopping

c. stress inoculation

d. rational-emotive therapy

Practice Test 2

1. Although Susan is an avid runner and vegetarian, her boyfriend abhors exercise. Susan breaks off their relationship because he failed to meet her expectations of health. Her intolerance of his behavior is called:

a. health promotion.

b. health bashing.

c. secondary prevention.

d. tertiary prevention.

2. What is the leading cause of death in the United States?

a. cancer

b. heart disease

c. HIV

d. accidents

3. Valerie finds that as she gets older, she has learned from her successes and failures and has learned to make better choices for herself, taking into account all aspects of a situation. What dimension of health relates to her ability to think more clearly?

a. social health

b. intellectual health

c. emotional health

d. spiritual health

4. The number of new cases of a disease or disability is called:

a. prevalence.

b. incidence.

c. mortality.

d. morbidity.

5. A holistic approach to wellness emphasizes

a. risk behaviors.

b. the integration of the mind, body, and spirit.

c. emotional, social, spiritual, and intellectual health.

d. individual and community resources.

6. Patrick adapts well to various social situations with people from all different walks of life. This ability relates to what dimension of health?

   a. spiritual health

   b. emotional health

   c. social health

   d. mental health

7. Which of the following is an example of *primary prevention*?

   a. using condoms during sexual intercourse

   b. attending a smoking cessation program

   c. going to physical therapy following an auto accident

   d. receiving radiation therapy for breast cancer treatment

8. When Bill decided to quit drinking alcohol, his wife supported him by not drinking either. This relates to which behavior-change factor?

   a. enabling

   b. reinforcing

   c. predisposing

   d. endorsing

9. After Kurt and Tammy pay their bills, they reward themselves by going for a long walk together. What type of positive reinforcement motivates them to pay their bills?

   a. activity reinforcer

   b. consumable reinforcer

   c. manipulative reinforcer

   d. possessional reinforcer

10. What percent of Americans aged 20 and older are at their healthy weight?

    a. 28 percent

    b. 42 percent

    c. 63 percent

    d. 79 percent

11. What component of health involves the ability to have satisfying interpersonal relationships?

    a. social

    b. spiritual

    c. emotional

    d. intellectual

12. You want to bicycle to get in shape but you don't have access to a bicycle. This is an example of a:

    a. cue to action.

    b. negative enabler.

    c. reinforcing factor.

    d. predisposing factor.

13. What behavior-change strategy involves learning specific behaviors by watching others perform?

    a. shaping

    b. modeling

    c. visualization

    d. reinforcement

14. What technique did Meichembaum develop to embrace behavior change?

    a. imagined rehearsal

    b. situational inducement

    c. stress inoculation

    d. thought stopping

15. Before Robert went to chemotherapy treatment, he practiced deep breathing, meditated, and gave himself positive affirmations, such as "I have experienced this before and I have only two more treatments to go." This is an example of

    a. blocking.

    b. thought stopping.

    c. stress inoculation.

    d. rational-emotive therapy.

2
Psychosocial Health

Chapter Overview

Psychological health is the interaction of mental, emotional, social, and spiritual dimensions of health. The status of our psychosocial health determines how we adapt to changes and face life's challenges. Mental health refers to the ability to reason, interpret, evaluate, and solve problems. Mentally healthy people respond positively even when things do not go as expected. A mentally unhealthy person may be irrational and have distorted perceptions that can make them dangerous to themselves and others. Emotional health refers to the subjective side of psychosocial health—the feeling side. Emotions are composed of feelings and patterns of feelings. Some examples are hatred, despair, release, joy, frustration, and love. The two most important aspects of social health are social bonds and social supports. Spiritual health refers to a sense of hope, purpose, and inclusion in a greater scheme of existence, among others. Some researchers define a spiritually healthy person as one who has had the following needs met: having, relating, being, and transcendence.

Our psychosocial health is based on our expectations and how we perceive life experiences. While some experiences are under our control, others are not. External influences include our family and friends, our support network, and the wider environment in which we live. Internal factors include hereditary traits, hormonal functioning, physical health status, physical fitness level, and certain elements of mental and emotional health.

Sometimes circumstances overwhelm us to such a degree that our psychosocial health deteriorates and we need assistance to get back on track toward healthful living. Depression has been called the "common cold" of psychological disturbances, affecting almost 10 percent of American adults. Anxiety disorders are another common psychological problem, affecting over 19 million American people. Anxiety-related disorders include generalized anxiety disorder, panic disorder, specific phobias, and social phobias. Six percent of Americans suffer from seasonal affective disorder, a type of depression believed to be caused by a malfunction in the hypothalamus. Schizophrenia affects 1 percent of Americans and is characterized by alterations of the senses, the inability to sort out incoming stimuli and to make appropriate responses, an altered sense of self, and radical changes in emotions, movements, and behaviors. There are more than 35,000 reported suicides each year in the United States. Suicide often results from poor coping skills, lack of social support, lack of self-esteem, and the inability to see one's way out of a bad situation. People intending to commit suicide often give warning signs of their intentions. Such people can often be helped.

Mental health professionals include psychiatrists, psychoanalysts, psychologists, social workers, counselors, and psychiatric nurse specialists. A variety of therapy methods are available.

NAME: _____ DATE: _____

TAKE CHARGE WORKSHEET 2.1

Emotional Intelligence Assessment

DIRECTIONS: Write your answers to the questions below in the spaces provided.

1. Are you aware of the emotions that you use to make important decisions?

2. Do you feel that your emotions are well managed, or do they sometimes get out of control?

3. Are you able to motivate yourself to accomplish an important task or a creative project?

4. Are you aware of emotions felt by others?

5. Do you handle emotions of others competently?

EVALUATION: Use the following information to help you assess your answers and to determine areas in need of improvement.

Basic emotions include fear, anger, sadness, and happiness. These emotions arise in varying degrees for different reasons. One way to handle anxiety is to determine the basis of your fears and whether they are real or imagined. If you find yourself irritated or frustrated, it may be due to unrealized goals or expectations that you deserve more than you get. Guilt, regret, and low self-esteem contribute to sadness and can create larger problems. Denying feelings of content- ment, joy, or appreciation can affect readiness and willingness to form healthy relationships with others. All of these emotions have a profound effect on our thoughts, decisions, and actions. Handling the emotions of others is as important as handling our own emotions. Emo- tional intelligence is a way of managing emotions so that they do not negatively affect your daily life.

For Further Thought

For more information on this topic, read this book: Goleman, D. (1995). *Emotional Intelligence*. New York: Bantam Books.

NAME: _____ DATE: _____

TAKE CHARGE WORKSHEET 2.2

Spiritual Health Assessment

DIRECTIONS: Answer the questions below in the space provided.

1. Was religion an important part of your upbringing?

2. Do you spend time meditating, appreciating the outdoors, seeking spiritual guidance, or reflecting on the meaning and purpose of life on a regular basis?

3. How frequently does your faith guide you?

4. Do you expect others to respect your need to worship?

5. Do you feel comfortable discussing your spiritual needs and activities with others?

6. In times of difficulty, do you ask a higher power for courage, strength, and wisdom?

7. Are you able to let some of the things you can't control be handled by a higher power?

8. Have you developed relationships with others who have the same religious or spiritual convictions as you?

9. When seeking a potential mate, is religious or spiritual preference considered?

10. Have you considered how important various religious values, rites, and celebrations would be if you were to have a family?

For Further Thought

Most of us develop moral standards (right vs. wrong) from our religious or spiritual upbringing. Changing one's spiritual orientation in life is very difficult. Is it important for you to share your spiritual interest with someone? Perhaps spiritual compatibility will enhance your relationship with another person. Take time to determine the significance of your spirituality in developing a relationship with another.

A good article to read about this aspect of the wellness dimension is: Chapman, L. (1987). Developing a useful perspective on spiritual health: Well-being, spiritual potential, and the search for meaning. *American Journal of Health Promotion*, 1, 35–36.

NAME: _____ DATE: _____

TAKE CHARGE WORKSHEET 2.3

Family Dynamics Survey

DIRECTIONS: Circle the statements below that describe your family of origin.

1. People in my family talk about their feelings.

2. People in my family listen to what others have to say.

3. Arguments about money are infrequent.

4. It is clear to me that the family is more important than work, money, or recognition.

5. I feel that my family members are close to one another.

6. My family members display respect and affection for one another.

7. Everyone has an important job or contribution to make for the family.

8. We often eat meals together.

9. Our family vacations are some of the fondest memories I have from my childhood.

10. My family members are able to express their opinions and resolve conflicts fairly quickly.

11. My family usually makes decisions together.

12. My family members are able to forgive one another for mistakes.

13. Everyone in my family respects each other's need for privacy.

14. There is no question that my parent(s) makes decisions based on the best interest of the family.

15. Our family reserves time each week for "family time."

EVALUATION: In the space below and on the following page, list family strengths that you consider important. Look at the items that you did not circle. How important are those characteristics? How would you determine whether someone came from a healthy or unhealthy family? What characteristics do you need to develop before you begin a healthy family of your own?

NAME: _____ DATE: _____

TAKE CHARGE WORKSHEET 2.4

Sleep Inventory

DIRECTIONS: Answer *Yes* or *No* to the following questions. Compare your answers to the statements in the Evaluation section.

Yes No   1. Have you ever fallen asleep in class or while driving?

Yes No   2. Do you consider yourself a "night person" (function better at night)?

Yes No   3. Do you avoid the use of caffeine, alcohol, or other substances after 8PM?

Yes No   4. Do you give yourself at least one hour to "unwind" before going to bed?

Yes No   5. Do you have difficulty stopping your thoughts at night so you can sleep?

Yes No   6. Do you have a comfortable bed and pillow?

Yes No   7. Is the room darkened when you are sleeping?

Yes No   8. Is the temperature about 68°F?

Yes No   9. Do you have a regular sleep time and wake time?

Yes No   10. When you wake up in the morning, does it take you more than 20 minutes to get out of bed?

Yes No   11. Do you feel sleepy during the day?

Yes No   12. Do you take naps during the day?

Yes No   13. Do you snore?

Yes No   14. Do you have tingling and numbness in your legs or move them about periodically through the night?

Yes No   15. Do you have a sleeping partner?

Yes No   16. Do you use any sleep aids to help you sleep?

Yes No   17. Do you get about 20 minutes of sunlight per day?

Yes No   18. Do you have any sleep disorders like sleepwalking, narcolepsy, or sleep apnea?

Yes No   19. Do you get at least 7–8 hours of sleep per night?

Yes No   20. Do you use the weekend to catch up on sleep?

EVALUATION: Sleep is a basic need just like food, clothing, and shelter. Without sleep, our lives can become miserable. The incidence of sleep problems and disorders is increasing to alarming levels. Some college students think that sleep deprivation and other sleep problems are "normal" in college. Once abnormal sleep patterns are set, they become difficult to change. Sleep problems can easily be corrected, but it does take some time and adjustments. Sleep problems, when allowed to continue, can result in absenteeism, illnesses due to lowered immunity, accidents, and accidental deaths.

1. Nodding off and falling asleep while driving is dangerous. You are more likely to be struck by a driver who has fallen asleep than by a drunken driver. Falling asleep in class may interfere with attention, memory retention, academic performance, and achieving future goals.

2. Some people claim they are night owls. In truth, they have merely set their biological clock to be awake at night and asleep during the day. This often happens when people work evening and night shifts. If you're having trouble getting up in the morning and functioning during the daytime, start going to bed 1 hour earlier at night until your pattern is set to accomplish what you need to do during the day.

3. Many college students complain that they can't get to sleep at night. One reason may be because they are unable to stop thinking or worrying about things. Another reason might be that they did not have time to "wind down" before they went to bed. The most common reason for being unable to get to sleep at night is caffeine use during the day. Stop caffeine intake between 6–8 p.m. The effects of caffeine last at least 2 hours.

4. Bedtime rituals are just as important to adults as they are to children. A bedtime ritual should be at least one hour long. It may consist of tending to hygiene, walking the dog, making lunch for the next day, setting clothing out for the next day, prayer, meditation, or reading a book. Watching television as a bedtime ritual is not advised because it is difficult to watch for only an hour, turn it off, and go to bed. If you are not able to do this, it is better to not watch television at all.

5. Before we can relax, we need to take care of business and be prepared for the next day. It is easier to get an assignment done than worry about it all night long. Make a list of things that you have to do the next day and forget about them while you are sleeping. If you still have trouble getting to sleep, try clearing your mind. You can do a number of things such as saying a prayer, counting sheep, or using a mantra. A mantra is a one-syllable word said repeatedly in succession while keeping control of breathing. For example, inhale deeply, and when exhaling, say the word "one." If other thoughts creep in, go back to the word "one." Before you know it, you will find yourself waking up in the morning.

6. Relaxing is best when we are comfortable. This means wearing comfortable clothing and controlling our sleep environment. The bed and pillows should be so comfortable that you look forward to "sliding into them." You may have to invest in a new mattress or buy some new pillows. If you have noisy neighbors or roommates, you can turn on a fan or some other type of "static" noise to shut out the disturbing noise.

7. Our brain tells us that when it is light we are supposed to be awake and when it is dark we should be asleep. A room that is not dark enough will make sleeping difficult. You may need to invest in some shades, blinds, or curtains to block unwelcome light.

8. The ideal room temperature for sleeping is 65–68°F. You will sleep better if the room is slightly cool. If you do not have control of the thermostat, keep a fan in your room.

9. Irregular sleep and wake times will confuse your brain and body. We need a schedule that we can depend on to function at our optimal best. In order to get 7–8 hours of sleep per night, a bedtime before midnight is best. If you have to stay up late, do it on the weekends when you can "catch up." Even though sleeping later in the morning sounds like a good idea, it can become a habit that results in missing morning classes or valuable time when you could have been productive.

10. Two signs of a sleeping problem are hitting the snooze button several times in the morning and feeling groggy when you wake up. There is usually a "morning fog" but it should not last more than 20 minutes. If it does, you need to get to sleep earlier at night.

11. Excessive daytime sleepiness or falling asleep when you're supposed to be awake and alert is something that requires immediate attention. One reason for fatigue is dehydration. We are more likely to be sleepy after lunch. One reason for this could be a "fatty meal" at lunchtime. Try eating a lighter lunch. If drinking plenty of fluids during the day, eating a lighter lunch, and getting to bed early doesn't help, you may have a sleep disorder that requires medical intervention.

12. Napping is not a good idea because it makes getting to sleep at night more difficult. Some people say that they can get by on 4–6 hours of sleep when they nap during the day. If you are sleep deprived, a long nap may be in order until you have a regular sleep schedule. If you are sleepy, getting up and walking about may help overcome the urge to take a nap. If you are unable to shake off the sleepiness, then a 20-minute nap is recommended. Any longer than that and you will wake up groggy.

13. Snoring is a sign of an airway obstruction, which means less oxygen is getting to the brain. A person who snores may find they have attention deficits, mood problems, or they are just sleepy all the time. If someone says you snore, you might want to find out why. Sleeping on your side is the first strategy to try. If that doesn't stop the snoring, then you may need to see an ear, nose, and throat specialist to check for nasal, sinus, or pharyngeal obstructions.

14. Restless leg syndrome will keep the sleeper and anyone with whom they sleep awake. If you wake periodically through the night, it may be because you work yourself up. Moving and thrashing legs about at night may be an indicator of a hereditary predisposition for Parkinson's disease. Restless leg syndrome can be controlled with medication.

15. If your sleeping partner has sleeping problems, then you will, too. If sleeping with someone else is a problem, suggest getting separate beds. If you can't sleep and you are irritable or angry at your partner, a different bed may be a good investment.

16. Sleep aids are not recommended unless all other methods have been tried. You can also take a hot bath or listen to relaxing music (with no words). If you are not able to sleep within 20 minutes, you can get up and do some homework. When you are tired, go to bed. If none of these methods work, you can try an herbal tea (no caffeine) or an herbal supplement (like valerian), but they do not work for everyone. Melatonin is *not* recommended.

17. Our biological clock, which regulates when we are supposed to be sleeping and when we are supposed to be awake, is regulated by exposure to sunlight. Artificial light just doesn't work

in the same way as natural ultraviolet sunlight. Just 20 minutes of sunlight per day can make all the difference in the world!

18. Sleepwalking, night tremors, narcolepsy, and sleep apnea are serious medical problems that can be very dangerous. If you are not under a doctor's care, you should be. If someone tells you that you do strange things at night, ask your doctor if you can have a "sleep study" done. It may ease your mind, or it may change your life.

19. Almost everyone needs 7–8 hours of sleep per night. Over the past 20 years, college students have reduced the number of hours they sleep to an average of 6.5 hours per night. Maybe this is one of the reasons why sleep problems and sleep disorders are on the rise. Even though we have busy lifestyles and demands, this is one area of our lives we should not cut short. It just may shorten your life.

20. Most people try to catch up on lost sleep on the weekends. If you didn't get 7–8 hours of sleep, you can make up for it within 24 hours. After that time, whatever sleep you lost is *lost*! If you stay out Friday or Saturday night, you may have the luxury of taking a nap or sleeping late in the morning the next day.

For Further Thought

For more information about sleep and sleep disorders, visit the National Sleep Foundation website at http://www.nsf.org.

NAME: _____ DATE: _____

TAKE CHARGE WORKSHEET 2.5

Assessing Your Support System

DIRECTIONS: Answer the following questions and circle the statements that could use some improvement in your life.

1. Are there people in your life who accept you just the way you are?

2. Are there people in your life who care deeply about you?

3. Are there people in your life who make you feel good about yourself?

4. Are there people in your life who are proud of you and your accomplishments?

5. Are there people in your life whom you respect and who will give you advice if you ask?

6. Are there people in your life who are willing to help you with important decisions?

7. Do some of your friends or relatives give you bad news or tell you things that would help you in life, even if you didn't want to hear it?

8. Would any of these people help you feel better when you are upset?

9. Would some of these people listen to you and try to help you improve problems?

10. Would any of these people be willing to share their deepest thoughts and feelings with you?

11. When you are lonely, do you have someone you can call or do things with?

12. Would this person go out with you on the spur of the moment?

13. Do you have friends or relatives who would go out of their way to help you if you really needed help?

14. Are there people you can call to watch your apartment or pet if you had to go out of town?

15. Would these people help you move?

16. Would these people lend you money?

17. Would these people let you stay with them if you needed to get away for awhile?

18. Would they help you if you were sick?

For Further Thought

Cultivating friendships can be difficult, but it is worth the time! If you feel that you do not have the support that you need from relatives and friends, what could you do to create opportunities for sharing and caring that might last a lifetime?

NAME: _____ DATE: _____

TAKE CHARGE WORKSHEET 2.6

Self-Esteem Survey

DIRECTIONS: Answer the questions below in the space provided.

1. Do you feel that you are just as important as other people?

2. Do you remind yourself of your positive qualities and use them to your advantage?

3. Do you take your successes into account more often than your failures?

4. Do you usually think you are as capable as other people?

5. Are you often proud of yourself?

6. Do you usually have a positive attitude about life?

7. For the most part, are you satisfied with yourself?

8. Do you respect your own needs and boundaries, and ask others to do the same?

9. Do you feel like your life has meaning and purpose?

10. Do you feel that you have admirable qualities that others might appreciate?

For Further Thought

Self-esteem affects how we approach people, our decisions, our actions, and the way we feel about our decisions and actions afterward. If we feel good about ourselves, it is easier to feel good about other people. Self-esteem helps us set limitations and boundaries for ourselves and for others, so that we are less vulnerable to things that can hurt us. A lack of self-esteem usually leads to problems in many areas of our life. What can you do to improve how you feel about yourself?

NAME: _____ DATE: _____

TAKE CHARGE WORKSHEET 2.7

Satisfaction with Life/Happiness Inventory

DIRECTIONS: Answer the questions below in the space provided.

1. What is your vision of an ideal life?

2. How close is your life to your ideal?

3. Have you achieved most of the things in life that are important to you?

4. What would you change about your life?

5. In general, are you satisfied with your life?

6. If you are dissatisfied with your life, is this a temporary condition, or a pervading one?

7. Is your happiness dependent on someone else's happiness?

8. Are you unhappy because of difficulties in the past?

9. Do you contemplate bad things to the point that they overshadow all the good things in your life?

10. Are you waiting for something to happen before you can be happy?

For Further Thought

According to experts, satisfaction with life is very important to being happy. One reason why many of us are unhappy is that, after achieving something, we continue to want more. As long as we do this, there will always be things that we want. Therefore, we may conclude that our life is not all that it should be. In order to be happy, we must make sure our goals are important, as well as realistic. If it is important enough to us, then we will devote the time and the effort to achieve that goal. If the time and the effort were not worth the goal, then perhaps it really wasn't what we wanted at all!

A good book to read regarding the importance of happiness is: Carlson, Richard. (1997).
You Can Be Happy No Matter What: Five Principles for Keeping Life in Perspective. Novato, CA: New World Library.

NAME: _____ DATE: _____

TAKE CHARGE WORKSHEET 2.8

Practicing Mindfulness

Mindfulness refers to the awareness and acceptance of the reality of the present moment. Cultivating mindfulness nurtures greater awareness and clarity in all you do. You can choose to bring mindfulness to whatever you are engaged in—eating an apple, taking a bath, hugging a child, walking to class, even studying for an exam. When we are present to the reality of the moment, our anxiety dissipates. If, however, we are dwelling in the past or worried about the future, our ability to live in the now is lost. We have only the present. The past is no longer here and the future is yet to be. Practicing mindfulness is interconnected with our spirituality and wellness.

DIRECTIONS: Choose one practice from the following list that interests you and try to engage mindfully in this exercise. Following your practice, journal about your experience.

mindful breathing

mindful eating

mindful walking

mindful sitting

mindful tea drinking

mindful listening to music

mindful reading

mindful cleaning

mindful gardening

mindful house cleaning

mindful listening

mindful speaking

For Further Thought

To read more about mindfulness, suggested readings include:

Nhat Hanh, T. (1975). *The Miracle of Mindfulness: An Introduction to the Practice of Meditation.* Boston: Beacon Press.

Nhat Hanh, T. (1990). *Present Moment, Wonderful Moment: Mindful Verses for Daily Living.* Berkeley, CA: Parallax Press.

General Review Questions

1. Define psychosocial health.

2. What characteristics do psychosocially healthy people share?

3. Identify four basic types of emotions.

4. What are the four major themes of spirituality?

5. Identify four types of anxiety disorders.

Practice Test 1

1. The aspect of psychosocial health that includes interactions with others, ability to use social supports, and ability to adapt to various situations defines
   a. social health.
   b. emotional health.
   c. spiritual health.
   d. mental health.

2. A mentally healthy student who receives a D on an exam may be very disappointed by her grade and will:
   a. reassess her course options and withdraw from the course.
   b. try to assess the reasons why she did poorly.
   c. make an appointment with the teacher to reevaluate the test results.
   d. become cynical about passing the class and stop trying to get an A.

3. Theresa is a holistic therapist who strives to be present in the moment with her clients. This relates to what theme of spirituality?

   a. interconnectedness

   b. living in harmony with the community

   c. practice of mindfulness

   d. spirituality as a part of daily life

4. What hormone is linked to circadian rhythms?

   a. dopamine

   b. serotonin

   c. GABA

   d. melatonin

5. A complex interaction of one's mental, emotional, social, and spiritual health is known as:

   a. wellness.

   b. psychosocial health.

   c. health promotion.

   d. psychosocial prevention.

6. Even though Sam is obese, he believes he can lose 40 pounds and keep the weight off. This relates to his

   a. self-efficacy.

   b. self-esteem.

   c. health promotion.

   d. readiness.

7. Eva dreads being in public and avoids social situations at all costs for fear of being humiliated. Eva is most likely suffering from:

   a. panic disorder.

   b. social phobia.

   c. seasonal affective disorder.

   d. generalized anxiety disorder.

8. All of the following traits have been identified as characterizing psychosocially healthy people, *except*:

   a. conscientiousness.

   b. introversion.

   c. openness to experience.

   d. agreeableness.

9. Marty flunked a math class twice and does not believe that he is good at math. He has resigned himself to not being able to graduate because he will never pass a required math class. This is known as:

   a. external locus of control.

   b. learned helplessness.

   c. posttraumatic stress disorder.

   d. exogenous depression.

10. What is the most prescribed class of drug in the United States?

    a. sleep-inducing drugs

    b. antidepressant drugs

    c. anti-anxiety drugs

    d. antipsychotic drugs

11. Zoloft, Paxil, and Prozac, commonly prescribed drug treatments for depression, are classified as

    a. tricyclic antidepressants (TCA).

    b. monoamine oxidase inhibitors (MAOI).

    c. selective serotonin reuptake inhibitors (SSRI).

    d. electroconvulsive therapy (ECT).

12. Two-thirds of all people suffering from depression are:

    a. men.

    b. women.

    c. adolescent boys.

    d. prepubescent girls.

13. Jack suffers from a form of depression characterized by alternating mania and depression. This is called

    a. bipolar disorder.

    b. schizophrenia.

    c. chronic mood disorder.

    d. seasonal affective disorder.

14. A person with a Ph.D. in counseling psychology and training in various types of therapy is a:

    a. psychiatrist.

    b. psychologist.

    c. social worker.

    d. psychoanalyst.

15. The onset of schizophrenia most commonly occurs in:

    a. the second trimester of fetal development.

    b. infancy.

    c. late adolescence.

    d. late adulthood.

Practice Test 2

1. The practice of mindfulness is a theme of:

    a. social health.

    b. mental health.

    c. emotional health.

    d. spiritual health.

2. Sam is fatigued and is sleeping too much. He has no interest in hanging out with his friends or family. In addition, he no longer cares to snowboard or participate in other hobbies. Sam may be experiencing:

    a. anxiety.

    b. a phobia.

    c. depression.

    d. posttraumatic stress disorder.

3. Abraham Maslow's "peak experiences" relates to:

    a. interconnectedness.

    b. mindfulness.

    c. subjective well being.

    d. self-efficacy.

4. What is the number one mental health problem in the United States?

    a. depression

    b. anxiety disorders

    c. alcohol dependence

    d. schizophrenia

5. Self-efficacy refers to the belief that:

    a. you can perform a task successfully.

    b. your actions are more important than your thoughts.

    c. your perception of the problem is correct.

    d. you do not need to make changes in your life.

6. One's sense of self-respect or self-confidence refers to:

    a. self-esteem.

    b. social support.

    c. ego.

    d. developmental capabilities.

7. What type of depression is associated with reduced exposure to sunlight?

   a. chronic mood disorder

   b. bipolar disorder

   c. major depressive disorder

   d. seasonal affective disorder

8. Every winter, Stan suffers from irritability, apathy, carbohydrate craving, and weight gain. He most likely has:

   a. panic disorder.

   b. generalized anxiety disorder.

   c. seasonal affective disorder

   d. chronic mood disorder.

9. Subjective well-being has all of the following components, *except*:

   a. psychological hardiness.

   b. satisfaction with present life.

   c. relative presence of positive emotions.

   d. relative absence of negative emotions.

10. What are the two most common psychotherapeutic therapies for depression?

    a. humanistic therapy and gestalt therapy

    b. cognitive therapy and interpersonal therapy

    c. psychodynamic therapy and family therapy

    d. cognitive therapy and psychodynamic therapy

11. A medical doctor who specializes in treating mental and emotional disorders is a(n):

    a. oncologist.

    b. psychoanalyst.

    c. psychologist.

    d. psychiatrist.

12. Steven has an intense fear of speaking in public and avoids many other social situations for fear of being embarrassed or criticized for the way he speaks. Steven suffers from what type of anxiety disorder?

    a. panic disorder

    b. social phobia

    c. specific phobia

    d. generalized anxiety disorder

13. What percent of people who commit suicide give a warning of their intentions?

    a. 15 percent

    b. 33 percent

    c. 50 percent

    d. 75 percent

14. What type of therapy assumes that people are good and have innate worth?

    a. psychoanalysis

    b. behavior therapy

    c. family therapy

    d. humanistic therapy

15. A therapist who attempts to restructure a client's faulty thinking pattern of perfectionism is practicing what form of psychotherapy?

    a. family therapy

    b. psychodynamic therapy

    c. humanistic therapy

    d. cognitive-behavioral therapy

3
Managing Stress

Chapter Overview

Total health is dependent upon connections between mental health and physical health. Stress is the mental and physical response of the body to the changes and challenges in our environment. Positive stress results from events we anticipate, like getting married, finding a new job, or moving to a new area. Negative stress results from challenges, such as financial problems, death of a loved one, academic difficulties, or the breakup of a relationship. If uncontrolled, stress may have serious consequences, such as the deterioration of mental and physical health. Relationships may become difficult. College students may find difficulty getting to class and grades may slip; if uncontrolled, these problems can interfere with future success.

The general adaptation syndrome, termed by Hans Seyle in 1936, is composed of three phases in which the body physiologically responds to stress. When we are exposed to a stressful situation, immediately our bodies experience symptoms that indicate the body is aroused, such as perspiration or increased heart rate. This response indicates the alarm phase. The resistance phase immediately follows, in which the body has reacted to the stressful situation and then must adjust itself to a more balanced state. The last phase, the exhaustion phase, is marked by the depletion of physical and emotional energy. Continued exposure to stress causes the body to compensate for the added strain on various body systems. The length of each stage depends on the susceptibility of the person dealing with the stress and the severity of stress symptoms.

Psychoneuroimmunology analyzes the relationship between the mind's response to stress and the ability of the immune system to function effectively. Stress may be one of the single greatest contributors to mental disability and emotional dysfunction in the United States. Both eustress and distress have many sources. These sources include psychosocial factors, such as changes, hassles, pressure, inconsistent goals and objectives, conflict, overload, burnout, and "isms"; environmental stressors, such as natural and human-made disasters; and self-imposed stress.

College students often experience stress when moving from a comfortable environment to a new environment. Roommate problems, lack of privacy, financial problems, adjustment to school demands, working, not getting enough sleep, feelings of inadequacy, and anxiety regarding classes are common problems.

Techniques for reducing stress include self-assessment, changing responses, preparing for stressful events, and setting individual standards and pace rather than trying to compete with others. Time management is a useful tool in developing a plan for achieving short-term and long-term goals, paying off debts, and prioritizing our lives. We can take care of ourselves through healthy eating, exercise, and daily relaxation. If there are things we cannot control, we can go outdoors, take a walk, or try alternative stress management techniques such as meditation, massage therapy, biofeedback, or hypnosis. Support groups are also helpful in getting through difficult times. In addition, development of spirituality involves practicing mindfulness in its four dimensions—physical, emotional, social, and intellectual.

NAME: _____ DATE: _____

TAKE CHARGE WORKSHEET 3.1

Stress Reaction

DIRECTIONS: Place a checkmark before the questions below that are true about yourself and/or your reactions. If there are other factors causing stress in your life, write them in the spaces provided.

Alarm Phase

_____ Do you get irritated by others easily?

_____ Have you said or done something recently that you wish you hadn't?

_____ Do you sometimes wonder why you over-react?

_____ Can others tell that you are nervous or impatient?

_____ Do you smoke cigarettes to relax or when you are upset?

_____ Other: _____

Resistance Phase

_____ Do you clench your jaw, grind your teeth, or have neck pain?

_____ Do you drink alcohol during the week?

_____ Do you need stimulants (like caffeine) for energy?

_____ Have you tried drugs (like marijuana) to temporarily escape?

_____ Have you tried drugs (like ecstasy) in order to experience pleasure?

_____ Are you experiencing sleep problems?

_____ Are you tired most of the time?

_____ Other: _____

Exhaustion Phase

_____ Do you seem to have numerous allergies?

_____ Have you gained or lost weight without trying since you started college?

_____ Are you usually sick when others are healthy?

_____ Do you have high blood pressure?

_____ Do you have high cholesterol?

_____ Have you wondered if all your efforts are "worth it"?

_____ Have you lost interest in the things that you once enjoyed?

_____ Other: _____

EVALUATION: Note the areas where you placed the most checkmarks. If most of them were in the *Alarm Phase*, then you might want to think of alternate ways to react initially to stress. If you marked more checkmarks in the *Resistance Phase*, you could be ignoring parts of your life that are important. Sometimes the things we do to escape stress only make the situation worse. If you marked many in the *Exhaustion Phase*, then your health may be suffering. It is time to take some serious action in making life more enjoyable, even if it means temporarily setting your goals a little lower. If you ignore the warning signs, then the problem will simply become worse. In order to manage stress, you must control it!

NAME: _____ DATE: _____

TAKE CHARGE WORKSHEET 3.2

Stress Tolerance Test

DIRECTIONS: Place a checkmark by the statements that irritate you. In the space below each statement, write what you can do to make yourself more tolerant.

_____ 1. A messy house, car, yard, or other personal space.

_____ 2. Loud music.

_____ 3. Waiting in line.

_____ 4. Being late for something.

_____ 5. When I get a stain on my clothes.

_____ 6. When things are not where I left them.

_____ 7. When I forget something important.

_____ 8. When someone makes me late for something.

_____ 9. When I put others' needs before my own.

_____ 10. When someone makes noise when they eat or chew gum.

_____ 11. When someone complains all the time.

_____ 12. When someone makes fun of something I do.

_____ 13. When people don't pick up after themselves.

_____ 14. People who never have anything good to say.

_____ 15. People telling me what to do.

_____ 16. People giving me advice I didn't ask for.

_____ 17. People with bad habits.

_____ 18. People with bad manners.

_____ 19. Someone who criticizes me.

_____ 20. Someone who is sarcastic.

_____ 21. Someone who makes me wait.

_____ 22. Someone who interrupts me.

_____ 23. A person who can't seem to leave me alone.

_____ 24. A person who always has to know what I'm doing.

_____ 25. A person who swears.

_____ 26. A person who never keeps their promises.

_____ 27. Someone looking over my shoulder.

_____ 28. A salesperson who won't take "no" for an answer.

_____ 29. Poor service from a service worker.

_____ 30. Someone telling me to do something that I don't want to do.

_____ 31. Someone who talks too much.

_____ 32. Someone who does not listen.

_____ 33. Someone who gossips about me or other people.

For Further Thought

Ask classmates or friends which situations irritate them the most. You might find that you can add to the list and that some of these situations irritate you too. You might find that you have things in common. Better yet, you might be able to laugh about some of the things that irritate you!

NAME: _____ DATE: _____

TAKE CHARGE WORKSHEET 3.3

Are You Overloaded?

DIRECTIONS: Write your answers to the questions below in the space provided.

1. How many hours are you in class each day?

2. How many hours do you work each day?

3. How many hours of sleep do you get each day?

4. How much time do you spend exercising, relaxing, or planning for the next day?

5. How long does it take you to get ready in the morning?

6. How long does it take you to drive to school, work, or other daily activity?

7. Is there someone else in your life who demands that you spend a certain amount of time with them?

8. What is the total number of hours for all of the activities above?

9. Do you find yourself saying "yes" to things that others can do for themselves?

10. Do you spend a lot of time during the day worrying about how you will get everything done?

11. Do deadlines come up before you are ready?

12. Do you underestimate how long it will take you to do something?

13. Do you take on tasks or responsibilities before you know whether or not you have the time or the skills to do them?

14. Have you found yourself apologizing for not doing something or doing something later than it was supposed to have been done?

15. Are you working on something important while others are having fun without you?

16. Are you worn out from all of your responsibilities?

17. Do you find it difficult to ask others for help?

18. Do you ask others for help or favors more than you should?

19. Have you missed important events in your life or in the lives of others because you had to do something that was overdue?

EVALUATION: Some people think that being busy means that they are important or that they are indispensable. The reality is that busy people do not accomplish more done than someone who sets their own pace. Time management, assertiveness, and setting aside some alone time may help solve the "overloaded" problem.

We have 24 hours in each day. Eight hours are spent working or going to class (or both) and 8 hours are spent sleeping. This accounts for 16 hours of your day that have already been decided. Now determine how much time it takes you to get ready in the morning, drive to work or school, eat breakfast/lunch/dinner, do errands, and the like. Subtract that time from the remaining 8 hours left in your day. How much time do you have left each day? Have you allowed at least one hour for yourself to relax, exercise, or talk to a loved one? Now, how much time is left for studying, writing papers, and doing research in the library or over the Internet? Plan on at least one hour per day for each class. Now, how much time do you have left for watching television, partying with friends, or some other "diversion"? If you do these things, does it reduce the number of hours you devote to something else? What is it you are willing to sacrifice? Take the time now to develop a daily routine that works for you. If you accomplish everything you need to do during the week, you will actually have time to do things you enjoy on the weekends.

NAME: _____ DATE: _____

TAKE CHARGE WORKSHEET 3.4

How Do You Manage Your Time?

DIRECTIONS: Place a checkmark before each of the time-management statements that might make you feel healthier, happier, and more productive. Ask others how they manage their time and add strategies to this list that might work for you.

Planning and Preparation

_____ 1. At the beginning of the semester, mark your calendar with the due dates for papers and assignments and when exams are scheduled.

_____ 2. On paper, break down each assignment or paper into smaller tasks. Begin working on each project at least 1–2 weeks in advance. Do this for each class.

_____ 3. Plan ahead for potential obstacles to completing your classwork, such as work schedule, social commitments, computer problems, illness, or family emergencies.

_____ 4. If you make a daily list of tasks, only put three items on it, and reward yourself for the things you get done.

_____ 5. Remember to plan some time for yourself each day.

_____ 6. If you are in a relationship, plan ahead for time to be together.

Task Management

_____ 1. Make sure you are fully rested.

_____ 2. Clean up the area where work needs to be done.

_____ 3. Select a time when you will not be interrupted. This might be early in the morning when others are sleeping. Let others know that you do not want to be interrupted.

_____ 4. Set aside 1–2 hours to work on things each day rather than trying to do it all at once.

_____ 5. Make sure you have all the materials you need for the task in advance.

_____ 6. Find a place where others are respectful of your need to be productive.

_____ 7. Leave a pad of paper so others can leave a note. You can contact them when it is convenient.

_____ 8. Get an answering machine or voice mail.

_____ 9. Turn down the volume of the answering machine so you cannot hear it.

_____ 10. When you start to feel sleepy, tense, or unproductive, take a 10–15 minute break.

Lifestyle Management

_____ 1. Limit telephone calls to 15–20 minutes. Get a timer if necessary.

_____ 2. Exercise at least 15–20 minutes per day (preferably outdoors) to stay in shape.

_____ 3. Get 7–8 hours of sleep each night.

_____ 4. Limit naps to 20 minutes, and take a nap only if it is really needed.

_____ 5. Limit social activities to the weekends.

_____ 6. When surfing the Internet, set a time limit and stick to it.

_____ 7. Watch only one hour of television per day.

NAME: _____ DATE: _____

TAKE CHARGE WORKSHEET 3.5

Developing Your Spirituality

DIRECTIONS: Spirituality consists of four dimensions: physical, emotional, social, and intellectual. Answer the following questions to assess your spiritual growth. Circle the dimension that you would like to strengthen.

Physical Dimension

Do I appreciate and absorb the beauty of nature around me?

Do I spend time outdoors walking, jogging, biking, or some other physical activity?

Do I interact enough with the natural environment (e.g., bird watching, stargazing, watching a sunrise)?

Emotional Dimension

Do I try to become more aware of the situations that trigger negative feelings?

How do negative emotions, such as anger and resentment, affect my body?

Do I practice thought-stopping, blocking negative thoughts, or focus on positive emotions via self-talk to help myself through a negative experience?

Social Dimension

Am I able to give and take in relationships?

Am I able to forgive and move on?

Am I an active listener?

Am I comfortable sharing my thoughts and feelings with others?

Intellectual Dimension

Do I take time to read spiritual literature and to reflect on how it touches me personally?

Do I take the time to assess significant events that have occurred in my life, their causes, and my involvement with them?

Do I ever examine my past roots to learn how I have gotten to where I am in the present?

For Further Thought

Developing the practice of mindfulness—the ability to be fully present in the moment—is interconnected with our spiritual growth. Your growth in each of the four dimensions of spirituality will enhance your ability to be mindful of the present and will contribute to your overall health and wellness.

General Review Questions

1. Identify psychosocial sources of stress.

2. What are the three phases of Selye's general adaptation syndrome?

3. Discuss the negative health effects of stress.

4. What are some tips for fighting technostress?

5. Discuss how physical activities can contribute to stress management.

Practice Test 1

1. A physical, social, or psychological event that causes the body to adjust to a specific situation is called a

    a. strain.

    b. stressor.

    c. resistance.

    d. coping technique.

2. What is the second phase of the general adaptation syndrome?

    a. alarm

    b. resistance

    c. exhaustion

    d. homeostasis

3. The branch of the autonomic nervous system that is responsible for energizing the body for either fight or flight and for triggering many other stress responses is the:

   a. central nervous system.

   b. parasympathetic nervous system.

   c. sympathetic nervous system.

   d. endocrine system.

4. Buying a first home is an example of:

   a. strain.

   b. eustress.

   c. distress.

   d. overload.

5. What section of the brain controls the sympathetic nervous system and directs the stress response?

   a. pituitary gland

   b. hypothalamus

   c. adrenal glands

   d. adrenal cortex

6. During what phase of the general adaptation syndrome has the physical and psychological energy used to fight the stressors been depleted?

   a. alarm phase

   b. resistance phase

   c. endurance phase

   d. exhaustion phase

7. At Bev's new job, there is excessive time pressure and responsibility coupled with a lack of support by co-workers. Bev soon suffers from:

   a. hassles.

   b. overload.

   c. conflict.

   d. burnout.

8. Stress that presents the opportunity for personal growth and satisfaction is called

   a. strain.

   b. eustress.

   c. distress.

   d. adjustment.

9. What part of the brain directs the stress response?

   a. hypothalamus

   b. epinephrine

   c. pituitary gland

   d. adrenal glands

10. Jack feels overwhelmed about interviewing for his first job following college graduation. To help him prepare for his interviews, his college counselor encouraged him to have several mock interviews with his peers and advisor to prepare ahead of time for this potential stressor. What is this stress management technique?

    a. meditation

    b. rational-emotive therapy

    c. biofeedback

    d. stress inoculation

11. During the alarm phase of the general adaptation syndrome, the:

    a. stressor disturbs homeostasis.

    b. body reacts to the stressor and adjusts to allow the system to return to homeostasis.

    c. body's adaptation energy stores release cells for energy and renew the energy reserves.

    d. energy stores are depleted and the organism dies.

12. What is the psychological system that governs our emotional responses to stressors called?

  a. general adaptation syndrome

  b. emotional response system

  c. cognitive stress system

  d. homeostatic balance

13. Which of the following is *not* a major trait of psychological hardiness?

  a. control

  b. commitment

  c. hard-driving

  d. challenge

14. After being trapped for hours in a collapsed building, Joe still experiences extreme anxiety and behavioral disturbances. Joe suffers from:

  a. panic disorder.

  b. seasonal affective disorder.

  c. generalized anxiety disorder.

  d. posttraumatic stress disorder.

15. Psychoneuroimmunology analyzes the relationship between:

  a. eustress and distress.

  b. internal and external loci of control.

  c. the brain and immune system.

  d. physiological and psychological stressors.

Practice Test 2

1. The adaptive response to stress occurs when:

  a. the body attempts to return to homeostasis.

  b. the stressor is no longer present.

  c. there is a sense of relief that survival has been achieved.

  d. resistance to the stress has adjusted to a positive result.

2. Positive stress that presents opportunities for personal growth is called

  a. strain.

  b. stress.

  c. eustress.

  d. resistance.

3. A balanced physical state in which all of the body's systems function smoothly results in:

  a. eustress.

  b. distress.

  c. homeostasis.

  d. general adaptation syndrome.

4. What pituitary hormone signals the adrenal glands to release cortisol?

  a. epinephrine

  b. adrenocorticotropic hormone

  c. melatonin

  d. serotonin

5. Dan and Judy are engaged to be married. This event may be a source of:

  a. strain.

  b. distress.

  c. eustress.

  d. adjustment.

6. A state of physical and mental exhaustion caused by excessive stress is called:

   a. conflict.

   b. overload.

   c. hassles.

   d. burnout.

7. Even though Tom experienced stress when he graduated from college and moved to a new city, he viewed it as an opportunity for growth. What is Tom's stress called?

   a. strain

   b. distress

   c. eustress

   d. adaptive response

8. Which of the following is *not* a phase of the general adaptation syndrome?

   a. alarm

   b. reaction

   c. exhaustion

   d. resistance

9. The third phase of the general adaptation syndrome is called

   a. alarm.

   b. distress.

   c. resistance.

   d. exhaustion.

10. What are the two branches of the autonomic nervous system?

    a. sympathetic nervous system and parasympathetic nervous system

    b. brain and spinal cord

    c. endocrine system and nervous system

    d. central nervous system and peripheral nervous system

11. What stress-fighting technique is a process that allows people to become unusually responsive to suggestion?

    a. meditation

    b. hypnosis

    c. massage

    d. biofeedback

12. What is the most important predictor of physical health?

    a. age

    b. gender

    c. mental health

    d. socioeconomic status

13. After five years of 70-hour workweeks, Tom decided to leave his high-paying, high-stress law firm and lead a simpler lifestyle. What is this trend called?

    a. adaptation

    b. conflict resolution

    c. burnout reduction

    d. downshifting

14. A stress management technique that involves self-monitoring by machine or physical responses to stress is called:

    a. meditation.

    b. biofeedback.

    c. hypnosis.

    d. deep-muscle relaxation.

15. What hormone stimulates body systems in response to stress?

    a. melatonin

    b. seratonin

    c. epinephrine

    d. cortisol

Violence and Abuse

Chapter Overview

Violence is composed of intentional and unintentional behaviors which produce injuries, disabilities, and premature deaths. Intentional injuries arise from acts that are performed with the intent to produce harm. Unintentional injuries are those that occur without planning or intent to harm. Women, children, and the elderly are groups most likely to be victimized through violence. People living in high-risk neighborhoods are more likely to be involved and killed by violence. People are often victimized in their own homes, by friends or family members, or in a neighborhood considered to be safe.

Poverty, parental influence, breakdowns in the criminal justice system, stress, heavy use of alcohol and other substances, cultural beliefs, the media, discrimination, oppression, and religious differences all contribute to higher rates of violence.

Some individuals have a lower tolerance for frustration and daily annoyances; others have the mistaken belief that anger should be acted out aggressively. If an individual grows up in a chaotic, disruptive, or angry household, they may believe that violent behavior is normal. The use of alcohol and drugs can exacerbate violent tendencies and increase the likelihood of suicide, assault, or homicide.

Assaults and homicides account for nearly 17,000 premature deaths a year in the United States. Hate crimes motivated by racial, religious, sexual orientation, and ethnicity/national origin bias are gaining national attention. Gangs cultivate aggression toward others and efforts are increasing to curb gang membership. Acts of terrorism have become a new public health concern at the national and international level.

Domestic violence is the use of force to control and maintain power over another person in the home environment. Unfortunately, it is a relatively common occurrence. It can involve emotional abuse, verbal abuse, threats of physical harm, and actual physical violence. Children may experience abuse that may be sexual, psychological, physical, or any combination of these.

Violent acts on college campuses include assaults, rapes, robberies, burglaries, and motor vehicle accidents. Freshmen are the most vulnerable college students. Parties can become unsafe for individuals unable to make good judgments due to heavy drinking or experimentation with drugs. Obscene phone calls, stalking, acquaintance rape, and other situations warrant notification of authorities. It is wise to be on the alert for situations where you may not be in control and learn to take steps to regain that control so that you do not become a victim. There are many things that can be done as an individual and as a campus community to prevent unnecessary violence.

Just as there are ways to prevent intentional injuries, there are also ways to prevent unintentional injuries. We can inspect our homes for potential problems, watch for hazards in the workplace and on the road, and examine our own risky behaviors.

TAKE CHARGE WORKSHEET 4.1

Are You Really Safe?

DIRECTIONS: Answer the questions below in the space provided. Assess your safety during class in either a large or a small group discussion.

Living Situation

1. Do you live near a busy street?

2. Are there streetlights near your building or home?

3. Do you have a motion light that comes on when someone approaches your home?

4. Where are you expected to park your car?

5. Is there a locked hallway that precedes your front door?

Unemployment and Crime Rates

1. Have you checked the Internet to compare the crime rate in your neighborhood? In your city?

2. Have you checked the Internet or newspaper to investigate the location, frequency, and types of crimes most often reported?

3. Have any of your neighbors been burglarized or mugged?

4. Does the community have services to help people who are unable to help themselves?

Neighbors

1. Do you know your neighbors?

2. If you were sick or hurt in your home, would anyone notice?

3. If you needed assistance while you were recovering, would anyone offer to help?

4. Do you have the telephone number of any of your neighbors in the event of an emergency?

5. How frequently do you visit with your neighbors?

Friends

1. How long have you known your friends?

2. How did you meet your newest friends?

3. Do your friends respect your need for privacy, respect, and honesty?

4. When you go out with friends, do they encourage you to do things that will impair your judgment or that are dangerous?

5. If you went to a party with friends, would they leave you behind or let someone take advantage of you?

6. Would your friends let you drive after you have been drinking?

7. Do you ride with friends who have been drinking?

NAME: _____ DATE: _____

TAKE CHARGE WORKSHEET 4.2

Hostility Assessment

Hostility is a combination of cynicism, anger, and aggression. Hostility can initiate aggression in yourself and others. It can be a by-product of frustration or high levels of stress. We may be able to recognize hostility in others, but we may not always be able to recognize it in ourselves.

DIRECTIONS: Consider the characteristics of hostility listed below. Write your answers to the numbered statements in the space provided.

Cynicism

Often referred to as "an attitude," cynicism is shown when a person behaves in a way that communicates distrust, dislike, or contempt toward another person.

1. Write down signs or indicators that a person may be cynical.

2. Determine if you are cynical. If you aren't sure, ask someone who knows you well.

Anger

Anger is an emotion that can range from displeasure to rage. It is an intense emotional state induced by displeasure, betrayal, or unfair, mean, or shameful behavior. It can also be generated by frustration, inconvenience, or annoyances. Actions resulting from anger are often justified or rationalized. Anger can rage out of control and become destructive.

1. Write down things that make you angry.

2. Write down what you do when you become angry.

3. Write down what you do when you are very angry.

Aggression

Many people are surprised to learn that aggression is not appropriate in all situations. Aggression is a forceful action used against someone to dominate or master them. This is appropriate in a game, but even the referee will limit aggressive behavior. We don't have to be aggressive to get ahead. Aggression can go too far. It can be used to attack, injure, destroy, or kill.

1. Describe situations when you might be aggressive.

2. Describe situations when someone might be aggressive toward you.

For Further Thought

To read more about these topics, suggested readings include:

Lerner, H. (1984). *The Dance of Anger*. New York: Harper and Row.

Williams, R., & Williams, V. (1993). *Anger kills: Seventeen strategies for controlling the hostility that can harm your health*. New York: Harper Perennial.

Source: Definitions were provided by *Merriam-Webster's Collegiate Dictionary*, 10th edition. Springfield, MA: Merriam-Webster, Inc.

NAME: _____ DATE: _____

TAKE CHARGE WORKSHEET 4.3

Other Forms of Hostility

DIRECTIONS: When a person is openly hostile, they usually exhibit several threatening behaviors. Below are scenarios of a person acting with hostility. Describe how you would react if you were confronted with a person exhibiting these behaviors.

1. A person with a negative attitude and opposition to authority who refuses to cooperate by being passively compliant or openly rebellious.

2. A person exhibiting behaviors of jealousy, resentment, or hatred over real or imagined injustices.

3. A person who slams doors, throws temper tantrums, or discharges other such behavior directly or indirectly.

4. A person who exhibits threatening actions such as destroying property, fighting, or frightening another person.

5. A person who is distrustful or suspicious because they fear others intend to harm them.

6. A person who is irritable, rude, or grouchy at the slightest provocation.

7. A person who argues, shouts, screams, swears, criticizes, or uses other verbal means to intimidate someone.

For Further Thought

It seems as though people are becoming more hostile toward others. What are some of the reasons for hostility? What are the consequences of hostility? How can hostility be managed?

NAME: _____ DATE: _____

TAKE CHARGE WORKSHEET 4.4

Anger Log

DIRECTIONS: Make three copies of this worksheet. For three days, write down each time you had a negative thought, felt angry, or acted out of anger. Some examples of angry acts include frowning at someone, honking your horn, gesturing, shouting, or doing something that would hurt another person. Use one page for each day. Rate your anger from 1–5 using the following scale:

1 = A little "peeved"

2 = Slightly offended

3 = Moderately mad

4 = Very frustrated or upset

5 = Raging mad

Day of the Week: _____

Cause of anger	Scale of anger	Your reaction after getting angry

Cause of anger	Scale of anger	Your reaction after getting angry

For Further Thought

Look for a pattern to the situations that make you angry. Determine how you might handle these situations differently.

NAME: _____ DATE: _____

TAKE CHARGE WORKSHEET 4.5

Victim, Perpetrator, or Witness?

A surprising number of people have witnessed or been involved in a violent incident. As many as one in four college students has witnessed three or more crimes in a one year period. Violence is hurtful, and the effects can last a long time. Take the following quiz to see if you are able to recognize abuse or violence.

DIRECTIONS: Place a *T* for true and an *F* for false next to each statement.

_____ 1. Any type of threatening behavior may be perceived as assault.

_____ 2. If you touch someone without actual consent and it causes harm, you can be arrested for assault and battery.

_____ 3. Abuse is something that occurs over a long period of time.

_____ 4. Abusers come from low-income families with poor relationship skills.

_____ 5. Emotional abuse includes the use of sarcasm, criticism, blaming, guilt, and fear to control others.

_____ 6. Emotional abuse causes the victim to be uncertain about themselves, their relationship, and their lives.

_____ 7. Teachers, coaches, day care providers, and other social-service workers are required by law to report suspected child abuse.

_____ 8. Sexual abuse can happen to anyone.

Answers to the questions are on the back of this worksheet.

Answers

1. TRUE. It is not important whether or not the accused person thinks they have threatened another. What may seem non-threatening to one person may scare another person enough to call the police, seek counseling, or make drastic changes in their life.

2. TRUE. Unwanted touching is perceived as a threat to many people, especially if they are weaker, younger, or in a subordinate position. Abuse of power will hurt people, and may result in physical and/or emotional damages. Many communities have a no tolerance policy, which means if someone accuses you, the police will handcuff you and ask questions after—when you are in the jailhouse.

3. FALSE. Anytime someone uses their power to hurt another person, it is considered abuse. Even one incident is enough for concern.

4. FALSE. Abusers do not fit into one profile. They may come from a wealthy family; they may seem even tempered in public, etc. Many abusers hurt others while they are under the influence of alcohol. While alcohol contributes to the problem, it isn't the cause of abuse. Abusers are often those who fear loss of control and often have low self-esteem.

5. FALSE. Actually, this is called verbal abuse. Often, abusers have low self-esteem, and they control others by lowering the self-esteem of others. Ridiculing someone in public indicates a lack of respect for that person and an intent to undermine their self-image. It is often used privately to wear down the other person or place them in a perpetually fearful state.

6. TRUE. Emotional abuse can take the form of not listening, ignoring, only giving affection when the abuser gets something they want, hiding important information, from their spouse, changing decisions after they have already been agreed upon, or doing things that create instability in the relationship. The abuser may think that if they keep the other person guessing, that they will remain in control.

7. TRUE. Many states encourage this practice because children who are being abused will protect their parents or caretakers because they do not want to be alone. Not every bump or bruise should be reported. If there are several injuries in various stages of healing and the child's story does not match the injury, other professionals should be consulted. The duty to report child abuse should not be in one person's hands. A third party should verify a suspected case of abuse before actions are taken against parents or caretakers.

8. TRUE. Anytime a person is drugged, forced, or subjected to an uncomfortable sexual experience, it is considered abuse. It happens in families, in youth activities, at parties, between spouses, and with people we previously thought were trustworthy.

NAME: _____ DATE: _____

TAKE CHARGE WORKSHEET 4.6

Victim Prevention

This worksheet will show ways to lessen the possibility of being victimized by another person.

DIRECTIONS: Place a checkmark next to the tasks that you are already doing. Place a + next to the tasks you plan to do in the future. Think of other preventive tasks that you perform and share them with others in the class. If some of your preventive tasks are not on this list, write them in the space marked *other*.

When you are alone, you:

_____ fill your gas tank during the day.

_____ lock your car whenever you are not in it.

_____ keep windows and doors locked even when you are in the house.

_____ carry a small flashlight so that you can look into your car at night before opening the door.

_____ carry pepper spray.

_____ maintain eye contact with someone you meet.

_____ walk with confidence.

_____ firmly say, "no thank you," and walk away if someone approaches you for something.

_____ do not stop to help someone you do not know; if you have a cell phone, call 911.

_____ always make sure someone knows where you are going, where you will stay, and when you will arrive and depart before travelling.

_____ keep a cell phone or calling card on your person.

_____ keep a yellow "need help, call 911" sign in your car for emergencies.

_____ don't go into a suspicious neighborhood without an escort.

_____ watch for others who might be watching you.

Other: _____

When you first meet someone, you:

_____ ask them questions to see if they can be trusted.

_____ learn more about them through friends.

_____ go to public places several times until you are comfortable being alone with them.

_____ invite them to meet your friends and family.

_____ observe them in many different settings.

Other: _____

When you are at a party, you:

_____ drink only bottled beverages and remove the top yourself.

_____ don't drink from a punch bowl or pitcher, or from a drink that was handed to you.

_____ keep your drink in your sight at all times.

_____ are wary of people who buy you a drink as a way to meet you.

Other: _____

NAME: _____ DATE: _____

TAKE CHARGE WORKSHEET 4.7

Workplace Violence Assessment

DIRECTIONS: Place a checkmark next to the statements of situations or behaviors that occur in your workplace.

_____ 1. Threatening conduct between employees or between an employee and their supervisor.

_____ 2. Intimidating telephone calls, stalking, or other behavior disturbing to an employee.

_____ 3. Extreme mood swings, depression, irrational/violent thoughts, and paranoia of a co-worker.

_____ 4. A co-worker with a preoccupation or obsession with weapons, the military, or hurting a person.

_____ 5. A prior romantic attachment with a co-worker.

_____ 6. A co-worker with recent excessive and unexplained absences from the job.

_____ 7. A co-worker with problems concentrating and/or inability to accept responsibility for mistakes.

_____ 8. A co-worker with increased signs of poor health or hygiene.

_____ 9. Increased stress in a co-worker's personal life, including financial problems, marital problems, or other relationship problems.

_____ 10. Inappropriate display of emotions on the job such as uncontrolled anger or excessive crying.

_____ 11. Indications of alcohol or drug abuse by a co-worker.

EVALUATION: For every item you marked, you should be increasingly concerned about a violent occurrence at your workplace. This does not mean that a violent situation will occur, but you may want to discuss some of these issues with your supervisor.

Source: Adapted from *Workplace Violence: Its Nature and Extent*. Office for Victims of Crime, Office of Justice Programs, U. S. Department of Justice.

General Review Questions

1. What societal factors increase the likelihood of violence?

2. Describe the predictability of future aggressive behavior.

3. Describe why some women find it difficult to break their ties with their abusers.

4. Describe the social contributors to sexual assault.

5. What steps can communities take to prevent violence?

Practice Test 1

1. Emotional reaction brought about by frustrating life experiences is called:
   a. reactive aggression.
   b. primary aggression.
   c. secondary aggression.
   d. tertiary aggression.

2. The most frequent sexual abusers of a child are:
   a. a child's grandparents.
   b. a child's older siblings or cousins.
   c. an adolescent male.
   d. a child's parents or companions or spouses of the child's parents.

3. The use of unlawful force or violence against persons or property to intimidate or coerce a government, the civilian population, or any segment thereof, in furtherance of political or social objectives is called:
   a. harassment.
   b. terrorism.
   c. ethnoviolence.
   d. hate crimes.

4. What is the single most identifiable risk factor for predicting child abuse?

    a. spouse abuse

    b. unemployment

    c. low socioeconomic status

    d. previous criminal record

5. What is the correct sequence of the cycle of violence theory?

    a. remorse/reconciliation, acute battering, tension building

    b. tension building, acute battering, remorse/reconciliation

    c. tension building, remorse/reconciliation, acute battering

    d. remorse/reconciliation, acute battering, tension building

6. According to the FBI, most hate crimes are motivated by

    a. racial bias.

    b. religious bias.

    c. sexual orientation bias.

    d. ethnicity/national origin bias.

7. Ellen and Tim are in a violent relationship. When Ellen tries to anticipate Tim's needs in order to forestall another violent scene, which phase of the cycle of violence are they in?

    a. acute battering

    b. chronic battering

    c. remorse/reconciliation

    d. tension building

8. Jack tells his wife, Melissa, that he is going to teach her a lesson and beats her until he feels that he has inflicted enough pain. Afterwards, he denies attacking her. This illustrates which phase of the cycle of violence?

    a. acute battering

    b. chronic battering

    c. remorse/reconciliation

    d. tension building

9. Which phase of the cycle of violence is also known as the "honeymoon" period?

    a. acute battering

    b. chronic battering

    c. remorse/reconciliation

    d. tension building

10. Acquaintance or date rape is most common among:

    a. minority high school females.

    b. new college women.

    c. mothers with small children.

    d. women in professional jobs.

11. Rape by a person known to the victim and that does not involve a physical beating or use of a weapon is called:

    a. simple rape.

    b. sexual assault

    c. simple assault.

    d. aggravated rape.

12. Research suggests that sexual assault is encouraged by the normal socialization processes that males experience daily. For instance, men and women are exposed to social norms that "objectify" women throughout their lives. What is this socialization process called?

    a. male peer pressure

    b. male misperceptions

    c. male socialization

    d. male attitudes

13. What percentage of women in the United States will be assaulted at some time in their lives by someone they know?

a. 25 percent

b. 40 percent

c. 60 percent

d. 75 percent

14. What is the single greatest cause of injury to women?

a. rape

b. auto accidents

c. mugging

d. domestic violence

15. Injuries that occur without intent to harm are called:

a. assaults.

b. intentional injuries.

c. unintentional injuries.

d. circumstantial injuries.

Practice Test 2

1. Anger that is goal-directed, hostile self-assertion, and/or self-destructive in character is called:

a. suicide.

b. violence.

c. reactive aggression.

d. primary aggression.

2. For an African-American man in the 20–22 year age group, the probability of being murdered is

a. 1 in 3.

b. 1 in 28.

c. 1 in 153.

d. 1 in 450.

3. When Jane began her new job with all male co-workers, her supervisor told her that he enjoyed having an attractive woman in the workplace and winked at her. His comment constitutes:

a. acquaintance rape.

b. sexual assault.

c. sexual harassment.

d. sexual battering.

4. Any form of unwanted sexual attention defines:

a. rape.

b. sexual assault.

c. domestic violence.

d. sexual harassment.

5. Risk factors for gang membership include all of the following, except:

a. high self-esteem.

b. history of family violence.

c. living in gang-controlled neighborhoods.

d. academic problems.

6. The assumption that men just can't control themselves once they become aroused defines which social assumption?

   a. minimization

   b. blaming the victim

   c. "boys will be boys"

   d. female masochism

7. In a sociology class, a group of students were discussing sexual assault. One student commented that some women dress too provocatively. What social assumption has this student made?

   a. minimization

   b. trivialization

   c. blaming the victim

   d. "boys will be boys"

8. The social assumption that sexual assault of women is rare is called:

   a. minimization.

   b. trivialization.

   c. blaming the victim.

   d. "boys will be boys."

9. Sexual penetration without the victim's consent is called

   a. rape.

   b. date rape.

   c. sexual assault.

   d. sexual harassment.

10. Most sexual abuse of children occurs:

    a. at the child's school.

    b. at the child's day care center.

    c. in the child's home.

    d. at the neighbors' homes.

11. What is the single greatest cause of injury to women?

    a. rape

    b. mugging

    c. auto accidents

    d. domestic violence

12. Rape that involves multiple attackers, strangers, weapons, or a physical beating is called:

    a. sexual assault.

    b. simple rape.

    c. aggravated rape.

    d. simple assault.

13. The phase of the "cycle of violence" where the woman is intent on anticipating the spouse's needs in order to forestall more violence is called

    a. tension building.

    b. acute battering.

    c. remorse/reconciliation.

    d. intervention.

14. What percentage of men reported that their wives engaged in physically aggressive behaviors against them in the past year?

    a. less than 1 percent

    b. 12 percent

    c. 33 percent

    d. 50 percent

15. What occupation has the largest number of worker fatalities?

    a. police officers

    b. truck drivers

    c. electricians

    d. military

Healthy Relationships and Sexuality

Chapter Overview

Good communication in intimate and nonintimate relationships is essential to good health. Because communication is a process, our every action, word, or other symbol becomes part of our lived history with others.

Intimate relationships are defined in terms of four characteristics: behavioral interdependence, need fulfillment, emotional attachment, and emotional availability. Family, friends, and partners or lovers provide the most common opportunities for intimacy.

Gender differences in conversational styles as well as differences in sharing feelings and disclosing personal facts and fears explain why men and women may relate differently in intimate relationships. Factors that play a role in selecting partners include proximity, similarities, and physical attraction.

Obstacles to intimacy include lack of personal identity, emotional immaturity, and a poorly developed sense of responsibility. Barriers to intimacy may involve the different emotional needs of both partners, jealousy, and emotional wounds that could result from being raised in a dysfunctional family.

Commitment is important in successful relationships for most people. The major types of committed relationships include marriage, cohabitation, and gay and lesbian partnerships. Success in committed relationships requires understanding the roles of partnering scripts and being self-nurturant.

Breakdowns in relationships usually begin with a change in communication. Most communities have trained therapists who specialize in relationship difficulties. If a couple's commitment to the relationship is strong, their chance of solving problems increases. Satisfying and stable relationships share certain characteristics. A key ingredient is trust. Trust requires predictability, dependability, and faith.

An understanding of sexual anatomy and physiology is helpful for deriving pleasure and satisfaction from sexual relationships and for making good choices regarding one's sexual health. Human sexual response is a physiological process that follows a pattern: excitement/arousal, plateau, orgasm, and resolution. Sexual orientation refers to a person's enduring emotional, romantic, sexual, or affectionate attraction to other persons and may be heterosexual, homosexual, or bisexual.

Sexual dysfunctions, the problems that can hinder sexual functioning, are quite common. Sexual dysfunction is divided into five major classes: disorders of sexual desire, sexual arousal, orgasm, sexual performance, and sexual pain. All of them can be treated successfully.

NAME: _____ DATE: _____

How Healthy is Your Relationship?

DIRECTIONS: Consider the dynamics of one of your closest relationships. Place a checkmark next to those statements that are true for your relationship.

Healthy Relationship

_____ 1. Treat each other with respect.

_____ 2. Feel secure and comfortable.

_____ 3. Not violent with each other.

_____ 4. Can resolve conflicts satisfactorily.

_____ 5. Enjoy spending time together.

_____ 6. Support one another.

_____ 7. Take interest in each other's lives.

_____ 8. Have privacy in the relationship.

_____ 9. Trust each other.

_____ 10. Communicate clearly and openly.

_____ 11. Each has their own letters, phone calls, and e-mail accounts.

_____ 12. Make healthy decisions about alcohol and other drugs.

_____ 13. Encourage other friendships.

_____ 14. Honest about past and present sexual activity.

_____ 15. Most people are happy about the relationship.

_____ 16. There are more good times than bad.

Unhealthy Relationship

_____ 1. Control or manipulate the other.

_____ 2. Ridicule or call names.

_____ 3. Dictate how the other dresses.

_____ 4. Fail to reserve or make time for each other.

_____ 5. Criticize the other's friends.

_____ 6. Afraid of the other's temper.

_____ 7. Discourage the other from being close to anyone else.

_____ 8. Ignore the other when they are speaking.

_____ 9. Overly possessive or jealous about ordinary behavior.

_____ 10. Support each other in criticizing people according to gender, race, ethnicity, sexual orientation, religion, disability, or other personal attribute.

_____ 11. Controls the other person's money or other resources (e.g., car).

_____ 12. Harm or threaten to harm objects of personal value, pets, children, or family.

_____ 13. Pushes, grabs, hits, punches, or throws objects.

_____ 14. Uses physical force or threats to prevent the other from leaving.

EVALUATION: Now, look and see where you have placed most of your checkmarks. If they occur under the *Unhealthy Relationship* category, do you think it might be time to find a better relationship? Look for, practice, and encourage some of the behaviors of a healthy relationship.

Source: This information was found at www.goaskalice.columbia.edu/

NAME: _____ DATE: _____

TAKE CHARGE WORKSHEET 5.2

Communication 101

DIRECTIONS: The most frequent reason for relationship problems is a lack of communication. How is it that communication gets distorted or misunderstood? Below, read the suggestions and pointers under each topic. Perform the tasks requested under each heading.

Conflict Management

Conflicts arise in every relationship. How the conflict is discussed and resolved may make or break the relationship. Conflict management consists of one person speaking up about the problem and the other person listening. Think of a problem you need to discuss with someone, and write it in the space provided.

Problem:

Speaking and Assertiveness

The primary purpose of speaking is to be understood. This means, *the speaker needs to make the message short while they still have the listener's attention.* See if you can *limit talking about the problem to 5 minutes* so that you have the listener's full attention. If you talk longer than this, especially about an ongoing problem, it may sound like whining, complaining, criticizing, or nagging to the other person. *Try not to use the words "you always…" because it sounds like blaming or criticism.* What the other person needs to know is how something they do affects you, and how they can correct it by doing what you need them to do.

It takes some practice to develop an assertive statement. An assertive statement consists of four parts. Study the parts and the example, and then, write your own assertive statement in the space below.

Assertive statement:

Part 1 "When you do … (mention the problematic behavior)" **Action**

Part 2 "I feel … (mention how their behavior affects you)" **Emotion**

Part 3 "Because … (this establishes the issue)" **Consequences**

Part 4 "What I would like is … (establish positive action)" **Solution**

Example:

"When you are late picking me up after class, I feel very angry because it means I will be late for work. What I would like is for you to be on time or tell me that you will not be able to come so I can find another ride."

Write your own assertive statement:

Listening

A message isn't much good unless it is heard. *All distractions should be eliminated.* Turn off the television or radio, or go to a quiet place to talk. Most speakers prefer that you look at them face to face and maintain eye contact. *Do not interrupt the speaker.* Interrupting usually indicates that the speaker is not important, and that the listener feels compelled to finish their sentences. By finishing another's sentences, the listener often makes assumptions about what the speaker is going to say, or indicates that they are listening to their own thoughts rather than focusing on the words being spoken by the speaker. *The listener should never say "I understand."* Instead, they may communicate understanding by paraphrasing or summarizing what the speaker just said for clarification. If there is a misunderstanding, it may be corrected immediately. The listener may be helpful, but *resist giving advice unless it is requested.* Try some of these phrases to indicate understanding.

After the speaker talks, the listener could say:

"O.K. You're feeling angry because when I'm late picking you up, you're late for work."

"It sounds to me like ... (fill in the rest using your interpretation/summary of the problem)"

"Let me see if I understand what you just said ... (fill in the rest)"

"If I'm understanding the problem correctly ... (fill in the rest)"

Remember, to the speaker, the most important thing is to be understood. The listener conveys this by not interrupting and by restating what the speaker just said and how they felt. The listener needs to seek clarification. The listener also needs to be empathetic (put themselves in the same situation with the same feelings). *If an argument begins, make sure it is stopped after 30 seconds before anyone says or does something they may regret.* Take some time to cool down, think about the issues, and try again. Make sure that you set an appointment for later when everyone is able to think clearly to *revisit the conversation or the issue,* and *keep the appointment.*

Communication Review

Below are the key points to good communication. Review these key points and try to use them when communicating in your relationships.

1. The speaker has identified the behavior which causes a problem.

2. The speaker tells the listener how the behavior and its consequences make them feel (basic emotions include mad, sad, glad, and happy).

3. The speaker tells or suggests how the listener can correct the problem.

4. The speaker gets to the point in 5 minutes or less.

5. The listener does not interrupt the speaker.

6. The listener checks to make sure they understood what the speaker said.

7. The listener indicates that they have also heard how the other person feels.

8. The listener presents another possible solution.

9. Both parties arrive at a solution.

10. Stop an angry conversation after 30 seconds and take a break for awhile.

11. Make an appointment you can keep in order to discuss the issue again.

NAME: _____ DATE: _____

TAKE CHARGE WORKSHEET 5.3

Is It Love or Infatuation?

The word love has two meanings. It can refer to a type of relationship, or it can be used to describe an emotion.

Love Relationships

There are different types of love relationships:

Phileo love is friendship love. It is a type of mutual admiration, respect, honesty, and trust between two people who hold each other in esteem and want to become affectionate. It does not have to include sexual activity.

Storge love is a practical type of love. When two people find they have much in common, including values, goals, and family background, they may reason that falling in love is something they should do. Over time, they learn to care for and appreciate each other in order to reach mutual goals in life. It is a type of "companion" love.

Eros love is an erotic or sexual love. When two people have decided to be sexually active after determining that their feelings for each other are very strong, they engage in intercourse. The experience of sexual activity stimulates a strong feeling of satisfaction and contentment when they are with that person. Without sexual activity, there is no love.

Agape love is unconditional. It is the type of unconditional love we all want, but it is hard to give and to receive. This type of love is usually found between a parent and a child. It is rare in mature relationships. If it is achieved, the bond is very strong.

The feeling of love usually includes: liking the other person, being happy, affection, tenderness, closeness, and attachment. Loving emotions may prompt intimate behavior. It may also be based on valued memories. It often creates expectations so that intimacy needs are met.

DIRECTIONS: Now that you have read the different definitions of love relationships, see if you can determine which of the statements below are characteristic of love and which ones are characteristic of infatuation. Place an *I* before those statements of infatuation and an *L* before those statements of love.

1. _____ Begins suddenly, becomes intense, then dissipates.

   _____ Begins slowly and gradually, developing over time.

2. _____ Enhances what you do and your relationships with other people. Does not hinder personal growth.

   _____ Occupies much of your thoughts, your energy, and your time to the extent that you are preoccupied while other important things are ignored.

3. _____ Creates an atmosphere of honesty, trust, and respect so that both persons can have other friends and activities.

   _____ Creates anxiety, insecurity, jealousy, and other uncomfortable feelings causing limited interactions with others.

4. _____ Usually is based on sexual chemistry.   _____ While there is attraction, the focus of the relationship has more to do with admiration of the person's qualities and not their performances.

5. _____ Has a sense of urgency.   _____ Is relaxed and trusting.

NAME: _____ DATE: _____

TAKE CHARGE WORKSHEET 5.4

What Is Intimacy?

DIRECTIONS: After reading each statement below, determine what you need to do to develop an intimate relationship. Write your responses in the space provided.

1. Intimacy does not require sexual intercourse. How can you avoid rushing into a sexual relationship?

2. Intimacy requires mutual understanding. How can you make sure that you understand each other?

3. Communal needs (togetherness) include nurturance, acceptance, and affection. What are your communal needs and what do you expect from the other person?

4. Agentic needs (individuation) include identity, self-esteem, power and influence, autonomy, and achievement. What are your agentic needs and what do you need to achieve them?

5. It is important that the needs of the partners are compatible. Can you meet the needs of the other?

6. Partners must be able to effectively communicate their needs in a non-threatening way. How can you do this?

7. Partners make an effort to listen to and understand each other's needs. What skills do you need to practice better listening?

8. Partners work together to generate creative solutions to problems. Are you able to accept the other person's possible solution?

9. Partners withhold anger because it is incompatible with intimacy. What can you do to express anger in a non-threatening way?

10. Partners create an atmosphere or climate that increases the likelihood of intimate interaction. What type of environment do you think is good for intimate interaction?

11. The relationship must approximate an optimal or desired relationship with another person. Have you discussed what the future would be like for the two of you?

12. Partners frequently share themselves with each other. The depth or intensity of sharing is something that is not shared with anyone else. Can you share? Can you respect the need for privacy?

NAME: _____ DATE: _____

TAKE CHARGE WORKSHEET 5.5

Are You Ready For Marriage?

DIRECTIONS: Using your own words, complete the following sentences on the topic of marriage.

1. Marriage is:

2. Love involves:

3. Most marriages fail because:

4. The most important part of a relationship is:

5. Divorce is:

6. The purpose of marriage is:

7. In marriage, sex should:

8. When it comes to making decisions:

9. When it comes to sexual intimacy, I:

10. I believe that money:

11. My goals in life are:

12. Affection should be expressed:

For Further Thought

Compare your answers with a classmate. See if they agree or disagree with your statements. Discuss the statements that differ, trying to understand another point of view, values, priorities, and expectations.

NAME: _____ DATE: _____

TAKE CHARGE WORKSHEET 5.6

Are You Ready to be a Parent?

DIRECTIONS: If you are in a relationship, make another copy of this inventory before you fill it out. Ask your partner to fill out one copy while you fill out the other. If you are not in a relationship, answer Yes, No, or Unsure to those statements you feel are important to consider before becoming a parent.

Yes   No   Unsure   1. I can trust my partner.

Yes   No   Unsure   2. My partner is honest with me.

Yes   No   Unsure   3. My partner respects my wishes and goals in life.

Yes   No   Unsure   4. We can talk about most anything.

Yes   No   Unsure   5. My partner is attentive to my needs.

Yes   No   Unsure   6. When my partner is experiencing difficulty, I am usually supportive.

Yes   No   Unsure   7. I would rather go to my partner if I have a problem than someone else.

Yes   No   Unsure   8. We are able to laugh together.

Yes   No   Unsure   9. We do not have to go out or spend money to enjoy ourselves.

Yes   No   Unsure   10. My partner and I try to bring out the best in one another.

Yes   No   Unsure   11. My partner is flexible.

Yes   No   Unsure   12. My partner helps with household responsibilities.

Yes   No   Unsure   13. I give my partner time to be alone or with friends on a regular basis.

Yes   No   Unsure   14. I can spend time alone or with others and my partner does not become jealous.

Yes   No   Unsure   15. If we have a disagreement or argument, my partner and I are able to resolve it relatively quickly.

Yes   No   Unsure   16. I get along with my partner's parents and siblings.

Yes   No   Unsure   17. We are in agreement about the number of children we will have.

Yes   No   Unsure   18. We agree about the time having a family would be the best for us.

Yes   No   Unsure   19. We are financially able to bring a child into this world and care for it for the next 20 years.

Yes   No   Unsure   20. My partner and I agree on how a child should be disciplined.

Yes   No   Unsure   21. My partner and I agree on the type of school our child should attend.

Yes   No   Unsure   22. My partner and I agree on how to save money for the future.

For Further Thought

Share your answers with your partner or a classmate. Discuss the differences in your answers. Now is the time to talk about it!

NAME: _____ DATE: _____

TAKE CHARGE WORKSHEET 5.7

Are You Compatible?

DIRECTIONS: Make another copy of this worksheet. Ask your partner to complete one copy, while you complete the other. Circle *Fine* for those statements you feel are true of your relationship; circle *Discuss* for those statements you feel need to be discussed. Sit down together and discuss mutual concerns.

Communication

Discuss   Fine   1. We ask each other about and share our experiences with one another.

Discuss   Fine   2. I am able to express my feelings without being criticized.

Discuss   Fine   3. Neither of us makes assumptions about the other.

Discuss   Fine   4. Neither of us "parents" or is "righteous" with the other.

Discuss   Fine   5. Neither of us lies to the other.

Discuss   Fine   6. Neither of us expects the other to read our minds.

Discuss   Fine   7. We both listen to each other attentively.

Discuss   Fine   8. Neither of us tries to interrupt the other.

Discuss   Fine   9. Neither of us yells or raises their voice to the other.

Decisions and Conflict

Discuss   Fine   1. We make decisions together.

Discuss   Fine   2. Neither of us thinks we have to be the decision-maker.

Discuss   Fine   3. Neither of us uses bribery or blackmail to get our way.

Discuss   Fine   4. We agree that we can disagree about some things.

Discuss   Fine   5. We try to resolve our conflicts quickly and make up.

Discuss   Fine   6. We do not bring up past issues during an argument.

Discuss   Fine   7. When we feel the argument is getting out of control, we take a break.

Discuss   Fine   8. When an issue needs serious discussion, we make a special appointment to discuss it, and we keep the appointment.

Discuss   Fine   9. We agree on whether to have separate or a joint banking account.

General Review Questions

1. Describe what we all can do to become better communicators.

2. Discuss barriers to intimacy.

3. Describe causes of jealousy.

4. Discuss the pattern of human sexual response.

5. Discuss how changing patterns in family life affect the way children are raised.

Practice Test 1

1. Intimate relationships fulfill our psychological need for someone to listen to our worries and concerns, also known as our need for
   a. dependence.
   b. social integration.
   c. enjoyment.
   d. spontaneity.

2. Lovers tend to pay attention to the other person even when they should be involved in other activities. This is called
   a. inclusion.
   b. exclusivity.
   c. fascination.
   d. authentic intimacy.

3. The type of family that includes unrelated people living together for ideological, economic, or other reasons, is called a(n):
   a. communal family.
   b. polygamous family.
   c. extended family.
   d. family of origin.

4. In the United States, the median age for men for first marriage is
   a. 22.3 years.
   b. 26.9 years.
   c. 29.3 years.
   d. 32.1 years.

5. After a painful divorce, Rick met a woman he was very interested in but held back his emotions for fear of rejection. This relates to what characteristic of intimate relationships?

   a. behavioral interdependence

   b. need fulfillment

   c. emotional attachment

   d. emotional availability

6. What percentage of all Americans marry at least once?

   a. 35 percent

   b. 50 percent

   c. 75 percent

   d. 90 percent

7. The ability to sustain genuine intimacy is largely developed in:

   a. marriage.

   b. dating.

   c. peer development.

   d. the family of origin.

8. Breakdowns in relationships usually begin with:

   a. unresolved conflicts over money.

   b. changes in communication.

   c. sexual difficulties.

   d. spending time apart.

9. The condition in which a person is born with both male and female sex characteristics is called

   a. gender identity.

   b. gender dysphoria.

   c. transsexuality.

   d. intersexuality.

10. Ovulation usually occurs on the:

    a. 7th day of the proliferatory phase.

    b. 14th day of the proliferatory phase.

    c. 21st day of the proliferatory phase.

    d. 28th day of the proliferatory phase.

11. Menopause is the result of:

    a. an increase in the production of testosterone.

    b. the presence of human chorionic gonadotropin.

    c. a sudden and permanent release of epinephrine.

    d. a decrease in estrogen levels.

12. In what structure of the male reproductive system do immature sperm ripen and reach full maturity?

    a. testosterone

    b. Cowper's gland

    c. vasa deferentia

    d. epididymis

13. Experiencing attraction to and preference for sexual activity with members of both sexes is referred to as:

    a. heterosexuality.

    b. homosexuality.

    c. bisexuality.

    d. homogeneity.

14. During what stage of the human sexual response does vasocongestion occur?

    a. plateau

    b. orgasm

    c. resolution

    d. excitement/arousal

15. Impotence is a(n):

    a. sexual desire disorder.

    b. sexual arousal disorder.

    c. orgasm disorder.

    d. sexual pain disorder.

Practice Test 2

1. What characteristic of intimate relationships refers to the mutual impact that people have on each other as their daily activities intertwine?
   a. need fulfillment
   b. behavioral interdependence
   c. emotional availability
   d. emotional attachment

2. Psychologists Jeffrey Turner and Laurna Robinson describe characteristics that make a good friendship. Which of the following is *not* one?
   a. trust
   b. confiding
   c. exclusiveness
   d. mutual assistance

3. Which of the following best describes the differences between men and women in selecting partners?
   a. Men are more likely than women to select their partners on the basis of youth and physical attractiveness.
   b. Women are more likely to select partners who are opposite of themselves in attitudes and values.
   c. Women are more likely than men to select partners on the basis of youth and physical attractiveness.
   d. Men are more likely than women to place greater emphasis on financial prospects.

4. According to Sternberg, the three key ingredients of love include all of the following, *except*
   a. intimacy.
   b. exclusiveness.
   c. passion.
   d. decision/commitment.

5. One important factor in choosing a partner is *proximity*, which refers to
   a. mutual regard.
   b. attitudes and values.
   c. physical attraction.
   d. being in the same place at the same time.

6. The practice of having monogamous sexual relationships with one partner before moving on to another is called:
   a. serial monogamy.
   b. cohabitation.
   c. an open relationship.
   d. common-law marriage.

7. Developing individual potential through a balanced and realistic appreciation of self-worth and ability is known as:
   a. trust.
   b. mutuality.
   c. accountability.
   d. self-nurturance.

8. A type of couples therapy that teaches crucial psychological skills that give people knowledge so they can help themselves is called:
   a. marital therapy.
   b. psychoeducation.
   c. relationship enhancement.
   d. marriage survival.

9. What percentage of people who divorce eventually get married again?
   a. 10 percent
   b. 40 percent
   c. 80 percent
   d. 90 percent

10. The tube that transports sperm toward the penis is called the

    a. testes.

    b. scrotum.

    c. vas deferens.

    d. epididymis.

11. Viagra® is used to treat:

    a. impotence.

    b. inhibited sexual desire.

    c. premature ejaculation.

    d. orgasm disorder.

12. What is the most frequent problem that causes people to seek out a sex therapist?

    a. erectile dysfunction

    b. inhibited sexual desire

    c. premature ejaculation

    d. dyspareunia

13. Which of the following is part of the *external* female genitalia of the reproductive system?

    a. clitoris

    b. vagina

    c. uterus

    d. ovaries

14. Tom's parents instilled in him the notion that "big boys don't cry." This generalization of males illustrates:

    a. androgyny.

    b. socialization.

    c. genderlect.

    d. gender-role stereotypes.

15. What is the average age of menarche?

    a. $9\frac{1}{2}$ to $11\frac{1}{2}$ years old

    b. $10\frac{1}{2}$ to $12\frac{1}{2}$ years old

    c. $11\frac{1}{2}$ to $13\frac{1}{2}$ years old

    d. $12\frac{1}{2}$ to $14\frac{1}{2}$ years old

6

Birth Control, Pregnancy, and Childbirth

Chapter Overview

Contraceptive methods are used to prevent pregnancy and sexually transmitted infections. There are barrier methods, hormonal methods, surgical methods, and natural methods, each with varying rates of failure. To evaluate the effectiveness of a particular contraceptive method, people must be familiar with the concepts of the perfect failure rate and the typical use failure rate to help them make informed decisions about contraceptive methods. Not all contraceptive methods protect against sexually transmitted infections. Barrier methods include the male condom, spermicides, the female condom, the diaphragm, and the cervical cap. Hormonal methods include birth control pills, NuvaRing, Depo-Provera shots, and Lunelle and Norplant. Surgical methods include tubal ligation for females and vasectomy for males. Other methods include the IUD, the "mini pills," withdrawal, emergency contraceptive pills, abstinence, and "outercourse." Fertility is determined by observing cervical mucus, rise in body temperature, and recording the menstrual cycle each month.

Abortion is a highly debated topic in the United States. Landmark cases addressing the issue of abortion are *Roe v. Wade* (1973) and *Webster v. Reproductive Health Services* (1989). Procedures for terminating a pregnancy include vacuum aspiration, dilation and evacuation (D & E), prostaglandin or saline injections, a hysterotomy, intact dilation and extraction (D & X), and RU-486.

When planning for a pregnancy it is important to be emotionally and financially ready to be a parent. In addition to focusing on the joy of having a new baby, future concerns should be discussed by the parents. Both parents should be physically healthy and able to care for a child. Some individuals may desire genetic screening to determine if they will have a healthy baby.

When a woman experiences breast tenderness, fatigue, nausea, and increased urination after missing a menstrual period, an over-the-counter pregnancy test will confirm a pregnancy within 85–95% accuracy.

Pregnancy typically lasts 40 weeks. The due date is calculated from the expectant mother's last menstrual period. Pregnancy is typically divided into three phases, or trimesters. During each trimester, specific developmental changes occur in the embryo or the fetus.

Labor consists of three stages and is managed by either medical or natural methods. The first stage of labor involves the breakage of the amniotic sac, the onset of contractions, and the dilation of the cervix. The second stage of labor consists of the expulsion, when the infant is released from the mother's body with the aid of uterine contractions. The concluding stage occurs when the placenta is expelled from the mother's body, following the birth of the infant within 30 minutes. Complications can occur during labor and delivery, even following a successful pregnancy. Sometimes a Cesarean section is necessary. This surgical procedure involves making an incision across the mother's abdomen and through the uterus to remove the baby. One in ten pregnancies does not end in delivery. Loss of the fetus before it is viable is called a miscarriage. Stillbirth is one of the most traumatic events a couple can face. A stillborn baby is born dead, often for no apparent reason. The unexpected death of a child under one year of age, for no apparent reason, is called sudden infant death syndrome (SIDS).

Some couples have difficulty conceiving or carrying a pregnancy to term due to problems such as endometriosis or scarring from pelvic inflammatory disease in women and low sperm counts in men. Fertility methods often used to help couples conceive include fertility drugs, insemination, in vitro fertilization, GIFT, ICSI, embryo transfer, embryo freezing, and embryo adoption programs, surrogate mothers, and adoption.

NAME: _____ DATE: _____

TAKE CHARGE WORKSHEET 6.1

Choosing a Contraceptive

DIRECTIONS: In the chart below, rate each birth control method using the following:

> SCALE: 1 = Not a concern 2 = Slight concern 3 = Major concern

Rate each method of birth control based on the nine issues below. After you have rated each method, total your score for each column in the bottom row. A lower score indicates a more favorable method.

Issue	Birth Control Pill	Mini or Morning After Pill	Male Condom	Female Condom	Contraceptive Film	Spermicide	Diaphragm	Cervical Cap	IUD	Contraceptive Patch	Depo-Provera	Abstinence
Side effects												
Allergic reactions												
Failure rate												
Availability												
Cost												
Morality												
Habits												
Prevention of disease												
The other person												
SCORE												

1. Side effects: Are you comfortable with the side effects of the method?

2. Allergic reactions: Are you allergic to latex, non-oxyl 9, or any other chemicals?

3. Failure rate: Are you comfortable with the likelihood of this method failing?

4. Availability: Can you get it without a doctor's prescription and does the pharmacy have it?

5. Cost: Can you afford to use this on a regular basis based on the number of times you have sex per week?

6. Morality: Are there religious reasons why this would be accepted or not accepted?

7. Habits: Would you use this as it was intended to be used without fail?

8. Prevention of disease: Would this method prevent transmission of bacterial or viral infections?

9. The other person: Would you be embarrassed to use it or would your partner not be cooperative?

NAME: _____ DATE: _____

TAKE CHARGE WORKSHEET 6.2

Fertility Quiz

DIRECTIONS: Place a *T* for true and an *F* for false next to each statement. The answers are on the following pages.

Male Fertility

_____ 1. Hot tubs can reduce sperm viability for males trying to conceive a child.

_____ 2. Marijuana has been linked to mutated sperm.

_____ 3. Smokers have lower sperm counts than non-smokers.

_____ 4. If a couple wants to conceive a child, the male is usually tested first for infertility.

_____ 5. Sperm can be frozen and artificially inseminated in a fertile woman with 100% likelihood of pregnancy.

_____ 6. Alcohol can interfere with erection and ejaculation.

_____ 7. Male chromosomes determine the sex of the child.

_____ 8. A male can not impregnate a female unless he ejaculates inside the vagina.

_____ 9. Sperm are viable for as long as three days inside the vagina.

Female Fertility

_____ 1. A woman can be fertile at any time during her menstrual cycle.

_____ 2. A woman may be more interested in intercourse when she is ovulating.

_____ 3. A woman has more mucous discharge prior to ovulating.

_____ 4. Women who take birth control pills for a long time have difficulty conceiving later.

_____ 5. A woman can become pregnant even if she is taking the birth control pill.

_____ 6. Nutritional status prior to getting pregnant can affect the health of the fetus.

_____ 7. Conception occurs in the uterus.

_____ 8. A woman's temperature decreases when she is ovulating.

_____ 9. The egg or ovum is viable for as long as five days in the fallopian tubes and uterus.

Answers

Male Fertility

1. TRUE. In order for sperm to be viable, it must be kept in the testicles at a lower temperature outside of the body cavity. Obviously a hot tub might "heat things up a bit," but that might hinder conception.

2. TRUE. Marijuana is stored in the body for several weeks. Any drug that is stored in the body will have a cumulative effect. Several incidences of mutated sperm have been observed.

3. TRUE. Smokers do have a lower sperm count than non-smokers.

4. TRUE in most cases. It is easier to test the male for fertility than the female because one sperm sample is quicker to obtain than watching a woman's menstrual cycle over several months.

5. FALSE. Sperm can be frozen and kept for many years. There may be many factors that can interfere with impregnation. No fertility method is 100% guaranteed.

6. TRUE. While alcohol lowers inhibitions, it also interferes with sexual performance. Depending on the alcohol dosage and individual response, alcoholic beverages can delay or prolong an erection.

7. TRUE. Females have XX chromosomes and males have XY chromosomes for determining gender. All male infants require an X and a Y chromosome so males are the primary determiners of infant gender.

8. FALSE. During sexual arousal, several glands produce fluids that eventually contribute to seminal fluid emitted during ejaculation. Even a small amount of this fluid prior to ejaculation can contain sperm and the woman can become pregnant.

9. TRUE. Sperm life is usually 1–3 days, depending on the acidity and alkalinity of the female vaginal environment.

Female Fertility

1. TRUE. Usually ovulation occurs approximately mid-cycle, but that does not mean 14–15 days before the first day of menstruation. Menstrual cycles vary among women and trying to calculate ovulation using the calendar method is not always accurate.

2. TRUE. All female species act differently when they are ovulating, primarily because of a surge in hormones that stimulate ovulation. They are more likely to do things to attract the attention of the male.

3. TRUE. An increase in mucous discharge is an indication that the corpus luteum has broken from the ovary and the uterus is preparing for its arrival.

4. FALSE. Each woman is different and each dosage of the birth control pill is different. Birth control pills are drugs and all drugs have different effects in different people. Some women get pregnant if they miss a pill just for one day. Others may take several weeks or months before they are fertile again. Since no tests of fertility are given before the birth control pills are prescribed, there is always the possibility that the woman would have had difficulty conceiving whether she had taken birth control pills or not.

5. TRUE. Women who choose birth control pills for contraception should be good pill takers. Birth control pills regulate hormones that regulate ovulation and menstruation so they must be taken according to directions. Skipping one day or taking the pill at different times during each day increases the chances of getting pregnant.

6. TRUE. Pregnancy can place a strain on any female, but a female who is undernourished or who lacks certain vitamins can have difficulty regulating her menstrual cycle or having a healthy baby. A very important vitamin is folic acid, a B vitamin. Many women are deficient in this vitamin if they have taken birth control pills or if they do not eat vegetables, fruits, and grains containing this important nutrient. A folic acid deficiency can cause severe birth defects such as spina bifida (the spinal column is on the outside of the body and the baby may never be able to walk, among other things). Women with very low body fat may have amenorrhea, making conception difficult.

7. FALSE. Conception usually occurs in the fallopian tube. It takes several days for the ovum to travel from the ovary to the uterus. Once the ovum is fertilized, it passes into the uterus and implants. Occasionally, the embryo implants in the fallopian tube, resulting in an "ectopic" (outside the uterus) pregnancy.

8. FALSE. While ovulating, body temperature in some women increases slightly, but it is usually not detectable unless temperature is monitored every morning over a period of time.

9. TRUE. The ovum is viable longer than the sperm. Ova can also be frozen, or fertilized and frozen.

TAKE CHARGE WORKSHEET 6.3

Your Genetics History

DIRECTIONS: Before you decide to marry or have a child, it is important to determine any possibility of genetic disorders. Discuss any known genetic disorder or health problem with your parents or other knowledgeable adult in your family. Write down anything you think might effect you or your unborn offspring later. Use the list below as a guide. Discuss possible genetic disorders with your instructor and class members.

Genetic Disorders

Cystic fibrosis

Down syndrome

Friedrich's ataxia

Hemophilia

Marfan syndrome

Muscular dystrophy

PKU

Sickle cell disease

Tay-Sachs disease

Thalassemia

Others:

Health Problems

Allergies

Asthma

Cardiac problems

Diabetes

Epilepsy

Hyperlipidemia

Hypertention

Learning disabilities

Mental illness

Mental retardation

Spina bifida

Thyroid disorders

Others:

ON MY FATHER'S SIDE there was (describe the problem and who had it):

ON MY MOTHER'S SIDE there was (describe the problem and who had it):

For Further Thought

Share this information with your prospective life partner. Determine whether genetic screening before marriage is a precaution you would like to explore.

General Review Questions

1. What three conditions are necessary for conception to occur?

2. What is unique about the fertility awareness method of fertility control?

3. Distinguish between the concepts of the perfect failure rate and the typical use failure rate in evaluating the efficacy of a particular contraceptive method.

4. Identify three types of fertility awareness methods.

5. Review the various considerations involved in planning a pregnancy.

Practice Test 1

1. Which of the following is *not* a barrier method of contraception?

   a. condom

   b. diaphragm

   c. oral contraceptive pill

   d. cervical cap

2. The calendar method is a

   a. barrier method.

   b. surgical method.

   c. hormonal method.

   d. fertility awareness method.

3. What technique involves making a small incision in the abdominal and uterine walls and then inserting an optical viewer into the uterus to view the fetus directly?

   a. fetoscopy

   b. ultrasound

   c. amniocentesis

   d. chorionic villus sampling

4. Jane purchased a home pregnancy test kit to find out if she was pregnant. A positive test detects the presence of

    a. HCG.

    b. LH.

    c. FSH.

    d. RU-486.

5. Toxic chemicals, pesticides, X-rays, and other hazardous compounds that cause birth defects are referred to as:

    a. carcinogens.

    b. teratogens.

    c. mutants.

    d. environmental assaults.

6. During the first stage of labor, the

    a. amniotic sac breaks.

    b. baby shifts into a head down position.

    c. junction of the pubic bones loosens to permit expansion of the pelvic girth.

    d. uterus works to push the baby through the birth canal.

7. Ellen is experiencing a sense that her pregnancy feels "real," a sense of wonder at hearing the heartbeat and feeling movement, and a struggle with new weight gain. These common emotions are experienced typically during what trimester?

    a. first

    b. second

    c. third

    d. fourth

8. What is the most popular birthing alternative in the United States?

    a. Leboyer method

    b. Harris method

    c. Lamaze method

    d. Bradley method

9. Which of the following lubricants are safe to use with a condom?

    a. baby oil

    b. hand lotion

    c. vaseline

    d. KY Jelly

10. During what stage of labor is the placenta expelled from the womb?

    a. first

    b. second

    c. third

    d. fourth

11. Which of the following is *not* a reversible contraceptive method?

    a. condom

    b. tubal ligation

    c. the pill

    d. cervical cap

12. For contraception, Alice uses a latex saucer-shaped device designed to cover the cervix and block access to the uterus. What reversible contraceptive method does she use?

    a. suppository

    b. female condom

    c. contraceptive sponge

    d. diaphragm

13. Stacey uses a method of natural birth control in which she examines the consistency and color of her normal vaginal secretions. What is this method called?

    a. rhythm method

    b. cervical mucus method

    c. body temperature method

    d. calendar method

14. What is the leading cause of infertility in women in the United States?

   a. pelvic inflammatory disease

   b. endometriosis

   c. vaginismus

   d. dyspareunia

15. The fertilization of an egg in a test tube followed by transfer to a nutrient medium and subsequent transfer to the mother's body is called:

   a. alternative insemination.

   b. in vitro fertilization.

   c. gamete intrafallopian transfer.

   d. nonsurgical embryo transfer.

Practice Test 2

1. A collection of symptoms that can appear in infants of women who drink too much alcohol during pregnancy, including mental retardation, slowed nerve reflexes and small head size, is called:

   a. teratogenic poisoning.

   b. fetal alcohol syndrome.

   c. Down syndrome.

   d. Tay-Sachs disease.

2. What is the most common genetic condition?

   a. Klinefelter's syndrome

   b. Prader-Willi syndrome

   c. Down syndrome

   d. sickle-cell anemia

3. The American Academy of Pediatrics recommends that infants be

   a. bottle-fed.

   b. breast-fed for the first 6 weeks.

   c. breast-fed for at least 6 months, and ideally for 12 months.

   d. breast-fed for at least 12 months, and ideally for 2 years.

4. The surgical procedure in which the female's fallopian tubes are closed or cut and cauterized to prevent access by sperm to released eggs is called:

   a. tubal ligation.

   b. vasectomy.

   c. hysterectomy.

   d. abortion.

5. What is the most widely used reversible method of contraception?

   a. diaphragm

   b. condom

   c. Norplant

   d. oral contraceptive pills

6. Susan experienced energy depletion, anxiety, mood swings, and depression for four weeks after delivering her baby. Susan most likely suffered from

   a. postdelivery letdown.

   b. post-labor anxiety.

   c. postpartum depression.

   d. secondary pregnancy.

7. What birth alternative allows the mother to deliver in a dark and quiet setting due to the belief that birth in a standard delivery room is traumatic?

a. Lamaze method

b. Harris method

c. Leboyer method

d. eclectic method

8. A 40-year-old pregnant woman underwent a medical procedure involving drawing a small amount of fluid from the amniotic sac to test for the presence of genetic abnormalities. What is this procedure?

a. fetoscopy

b. amniocentesis

c. sonography

d. chorionic villus sampling

9. What is the most commonly used method of first-trimester abortion?

a. dilation and evacuation

b. vacuum aspiration

c. dilation and curettage

d. saline induction

10. Most oral contraceptives work through the:

a. use of synthetic follicle-stimulating hormones.

b. combined effects of synthetic estrogen and progesterone.

c. combined effects of synthetic testosterone and follicle-stimulating hormones.

d. use of estrogen-only hormones.

11. Depo-Provera:

a. must be taken orally every 24 hours.

b. consists of six silicone capsules that contain progesterone.

c. is a long-acting synthetic progesterone that is injected intramuscularly every three months.

d. must be inserted in the vagina at least 15 minutes prior to intercourse and left in place at least six hours afterwards.

12. Which of the following illustrates nonsurgical embryo transfer?

a. in vitro fertilization of a donor egg by the husband's sperm and subsequent transfer to the wife's uterus

b. replacing the nucleus of an in vitro fertilized egg with the nucleus of a donor cell

c. fertilization by depositing partner's semen into a woman's vagina through a tube

d. artificial insemination of a donor or with husband's sperm

13. How many American couples experience infertility?

a. 1 in 6

b. 1 in 24

c. 1 in 60

d. 1 in 100

14. What disease is caused by an organism found in cat feces that, when contracted by a pregnant woman, may result in stillbirth?

a. Down syndrome

b. toxoplasmosis

c. Klinefelter's syndrome

d. Prader-Willi syndrome

15. When is the period of greatest fetal growth?

a. first trimester

b. second trimester

c. third trimester

d. "fourth trimester"

7
Licit and Illicit Drugs

Chapter Overview

Drugs are categorized as prescription, over-the-counter (OTC), recreational, herbal, illicit, and commercial. The classifications are based primarily on how the drug acts on the body. Each drug category has psychoactive drugs that alter mood or behavior. Drugs can be taken orally, intravenously, intramuscularly, subcutaneously, by inhalation, inunction (absorption), or through suppositories.

Addiction is continued involvement with a substance or activity despite ongoing negative consequences. To be addictive, a behavior must have the potential to produce a positive mood change. All addictions have four symptoms: compulsion, loss of control, negative consequences, and denial.

Antibiotics, sedatives, tranquilizers, and antidepressants are common prescription drugs and come in both brand name and generic form. OTC drugs generally have less adverse effects but are still as effective and powerful as prescription drugs. Analgesics, cold/cough/allergy/asthma medicines, stimulants, sleeping aids, and dieting aids can be purchased without a prescription. When using OTC medications, it is important to identify the active ingredients, read warnings, and not use them for more than one to two weeks. Use caution when taking OTC and prescription medications together as a synergistic effect, antagonistic effect, intolerance, or cross-tolerance is possible.

Illicit drugs are those drugs that are illegal to possess, produce, or sell. In 2002, about 19.5 million Americans were illicit drug users, about half the number of users from 1979. Among youth, however, illicit drug use has been increasing in recent years. Drugs are classified into five schedules, based on their potential for abuse, their medical uses, and accepted standards of safe use. Schedule I drugs are those with the highest potential for abuse and have no valid medical uses. Schedules, II, III, IV, and V drugs have known and accepted medical uses; however, many of them present serious health threats when abused or misused. Illicit drugs can be divided into seven categories: stimulants, marijuana and its derivatives, depressants, hallucinogens/psychedelics, designer drugs, inhalants, and steroids.

Illegal drug use in the United States places a burden on our economy due to the cost of prevention and treatment programs, health care costs, reduced job productivity, lost earnings, increased demand for social care, and increased crime. Drugs are a major problem in the workplace. Workplace drug testing is one proposed solution to this problem.

NAME: _____ DATE: _____

TAKE CHARGE WORKSHEET 7.1

What Is Substance Abuse?

DIRECTIONS: Think of a substance you use quite regularly and determine whether you are properly using, misusing, abusing, or addicted to the substance. Examples of substances include caffeine (soft drinks, coffee, tea, chocolate, energy drinks, NoDoz®, Jolt™, Vivarin®, and any products containing guarana), nicotine (snuff, chewing tobacco, cigarettes, cigars, pipe), over-the-counter medicines, prescription medicines, alcohol, marijuana, cocaine, ecstasy, or other psychoactive or pain relieving drugs. Check the things that apply to you and your use of the drug.

Substance Use

_____ When you use this substance, do you usually use it for less than three days?

_____ Are you taking the drug for the reason it was intended?

_____ Are you aware of the side effects associated with the drug?

_____ Are you using the drug according to instructions?

Substance Misuse

_____ Have you taken this drug for reasons other than intended?

_____ Do you use this drug while taking other drugs?

_____ Are you taking another drug prescribed to someone else or giving your prescription drugs to someone else?

_____ Have you avoided reporting problems, side effects, and other medications to your doctor?

_____ When you use this substance, do you take a little more than the instructions say?

Substance Abuse

_____ Have you been using the drug longer than another person might use it?

_____ Are you hiding the fact that you are using this drug?

_____ When you use the drug, do you find yourself using more and more of it?

_____ When you take the drug, do you have to use more of it to get the same effect you began using it for in the first place?

_____ Do you black out or have trouble remembering what happened when you used the drug?

_____ Have you become violent or hurt another person/thing while under the influence of the drug?

_____ Has your academic, work, or other performance deteriorated since you started using the drug?

Substance Addiction

_____ Do you have cravings for the drug?

_____ Do you have withdrawal symptoms if you are not using the drug?

_____ Do you begin using the drug as soon as you get up in the morning?

_____ When you buy the drug, do you buy it in large quantities?

_____ Does a substantial portion of your income or living expenses go toward the purchase of the drug?

_____ Have you lied to your friends about your use of the drug?

_____ Have you tried to hide how you are using the drug from others?

_____ Have your borrowed money from friends, family, or casual acquaintances to buy the drug?

_____ Has anyone approached you saying they are concerned about you and that you might have a problem?

_____ Have you heard yourself denying that you have a problem to someone else?

_____ Has use of this drug interfered with your social, work, or school obligations?

_____ Are you unable to function "normally" without the drug?

_____ Have you started thinking about seeing a counselor, going to Alcoholics Anonymous (AA) meetings, or investigating a rehabilitation center?

Solutions for Substance Misuse or Abuse

If you appear to be misusing or abusing the substance, make an effort to reduce how often you use it. Strategies below can be used to help you become a moderate user.

Caffeine

Normal use would be 1–2 cups of coffee, tea, or soda drinks (citrus or cola). You could reduce caffeine usage by:

1. Switching to a beverage that has less caffeine content. Instant coffee has less than automatic drip, and automatic drip has less than cappuccino or espresso. Green tea has less caffeine than black tea, either brewed or instant. Brew tea for a shorter amount of time (3–5 minutes maximum).

2. Drink caffeinated drinks only when you need them during the day. Drink them 30 minutes before you need the caffeine to work. Remember that the effects wear off after 2–3 hours.

3. When you become tired, go outside and take a brisk walk or jog. Get some sunlight or change your environment. You will be surprised how energized you will become and how your need for caffeine is forgotten.

4. Remember that caffeine is a diuretic and will make you dehydrated. We often confuse the thirst signal as a need to eat. Drink water to make up for the water you lose.

5. Caffeine often causes an upset stomach. We feel better after we eat. Wait as long as you can before you use the caffeine so you will eat fewer snacks.

6. Do not drink caffeinated beverages with meals or after 8:00 p.m. It will interfere with normal sleeping patterns and you will experience daytime sleepiness that will lead you to more caffeine.

7. Start drinking more water, fruit juices, and milk. They are more nutritious.

Smoking (or Dipping)

Most people begin smoking thinking it is a relatively harmless habit until they take on a smoker's lifestyle and devote many dollars to it. It may take several times before you actually quit smoking/dipping and become a successful non-user. Remember that you are not a non-user unless you haven't had a cigarette/dip in more than a year. You can become a non-smoker by:

1. Start by looking at the amount of nicotine in each cigarette/dip you smoke/use. Keep a log/journal/diary to help you analyze your habit. Determine the times of day/night that you are most likely to use it, the situations you are most likely to use it in, and what triggers the urge to use it. Once you see the pattern, you can find ways to divert use of the substance.

2. If you are more likely to smoke/dip first thing in the morning out of habit, develop a new morning routine. Delay that first cigarette/dip as long as you can.

3. If you smoke/dip because you enjoy it, you need to break the pleasure cycle. Switch to a different brand that you don't like. If you prefer menthols, get regular. If you prefer long ones, buy short ones. If you prefer lights, switch to something heavier.

4. If your friends smoke/dip, ask them not to do it around you. You may have to find some new non-using friends. Avoid smoky atmospheres as much as possible.

5. If you smoke/dip because you are bored or need stimulation, think of other things you can do. Start playing basketball, try in-line skating, or some other activity you can't do while you're smoking.

6. If you smoke when you are driving, keep gum, sunflower seeds, bottled water, mints, or something else in the car so it is within easy reach. Listen to a relaxing CD if you are anxious or an energizing CD if you need a lift.

7. If you smoke when you are on the telephone, limit conversations to 3 minutes or less. Scribble on a doodle pad to keep your hands busy.

8. Many times the urge to smoke/dip is confused with the thirst signals. Instead of smoking/dipping, try drinking water. You need 48–64 ounces of fluids per day anyway.

9. Stop buying cigarettes/chew/snuff. If you have an uncontrollable urge to buy them, remember that all urges will pass. Close your eyes, clear your mind so you're not thinking about anything (especially smoking), inhale slowly and deeply, and visualize yourself smelling good, tasting good food, and kissing someone you like without feeling embarrassed by smoker's breath.

10. Set a quit date, tell everyone about it, and then stop. Tell yourself that after 3 days you are over the worst of it and the next goal is to not get started again. If you are able to achieve this, reward yourself. Spend the money that you normally would have spent on tobacco products on something you normally wouldn't spend it on.

Alcohol Drinking

Binge drinking would be 5 or more drinks in one evening for men. Moderate drinking for men would be 3–4 drinks. Binge drinking for women would be 4 or more drinks in one evening. Moderate drinking for females would be 1–2 drinks. Strategies to reduce alcohol intake include:

1. Tell friends that you will go out with them only on Friday and Saturday nights.

2. Limit the number of drinks you drink each time.

3. Eat something when you drink. Food will slow down absorption of the alcohol. When you are eating, you usually do less drinking.

4. Drink a non-alcoholic drink after each alcoholic drink. Avoid carbonated beverages because the carbonation speeds up absorption and metabolism of the alcohol.

5. Tell friends that you are controlling your weight by drinking things with fewer calories. Try club soda with lime, a Virgin Mary, a "light" beer, tonic water with lemon, or orange juice with grenadine. You may start a new trend.

6. Offer to be a designated driver.

7. If your friends still buy you drinks, order drinks by the pitcher, or do other things to encourage you to drink when you're trying to cut back, find other friends.

8. Find other things to do besides go out to bars or to parties where people are drinking alcohol.

NAME: _____ DATE: _____

TAKE CHARGE WORKSHEET 7.2

Substance Use Log

DIRECTIONS: For one week (Monday through Sunday), monitor your use of any recreational, over-the-counter, prescription, or psychoactive drug. Use the log sheet below. An example is provided in the first line of the log sheet. *You may need more than one copy. Make as many as you think you will need.*

Over-the-counter drugs include stimulants (NoDoz®, Vivarin®, Yellow Jackets®), supplements (herbal or weight loss), ergogenic aids (weight gain or muscle building powders or drinks), pain relievers (aspirin, acetaminophen, ibuprofen, naproxyn sodium), sinus medications (nasal sprays, tablets), cough syrups (containing codeine), diet pills, or any inhalant (aerosol spray).

Prescription drugs include birth control pills, antibiotics, pain relievers, allergy medications, anti-depressants, tranquilizers, stimulants for ADD or ADHD, or anything prescribed by a physician.

Socially accepted drugs include caffeine, nicotine, and alcohol.

Recreational drugs include marijuana, Ecstasy, GHB, cocaine, crack, "designer" or "club drugs."

Psychoactive drugs are drugs that affect the mind, emotions, and feelings such as LSD, peyote, mushrooms, or heroin.

Date and Day of the Week	Substance Used	Time of Day	Feelings Before	Amount	Reasons for Use

Use the log sheets to analyze your behavior to reduce or eliminate it. After you have seven days of log sheets, answer the following questions.

1. Does your substance use match one of these problems? If so, which one?

   Substance Misuse = Taking a substance for purpose other than what it was intended.

   Substance Abuse = Taking a substance in high doses frequently due to an increased tolerance and physical or psychological addiction.

2. If the substance was a prescription medicine, did you take it the same time every day and as instructed?

3. If the substance was an over-the-counter product, where did you get your information on how to use this product?

4. What occurred immediately prior to using the substance that potentially triggered your urge or need for the substance?

5. What feelings prompted you to use the substance? When were the feelings most likely to occur?

6. How often does this urge occur?

7. What situation would you need to avoid if you wanted to reduce or eliminate use of the substance?

8. What communication or social skills would you need to use to reduce use of the substance?

9. What behavior could you substitute for the substance you are using?

NAME: _____ DATE: _____

TAKE CHARGE WORKSHEET 7.3

Test Your Drug I.Q.

DIRECTIONS: Fill in the blanks in the statements below using the following terms.

TERMS:

addicted	denial	lifelong	screened
advice from friends	dependence	nicotine	seduction
alcohol	genetic predisposition	opium	self-destruction
arrested	increased body	parents	several weeks
dangerous	temperature	pleasure	testosterone
dehydration	inhaling	risk taking	tolerance

1. Most individuals are motivated to use drugs because many of our actions are motivated by

   the desire to increase _____ and decrease pain.

2. There are various theories about why people use drugs, including _____,

   _____, _____, and _____.

3. The most abused drugs in the United States are _____ and _____.

4. The drug responsible for killing more Americans than any other drug is _____.

5. The most common symptom displayed by those who abuse drugs is _____.

6. A person is _____ to a drug when they experience withdrawal symptoms without
   its use.

7. _____ is a term used to describe when a person increases the amount of the drug
   used to achieve the same effect as when they first used it.

8. The quickest way for the effects of a drug to reach the brain is by _____ it.

9. Drugs distributed in many clubs and recreational areas such as methamphetamine, Ecstasy,

   and GHB are _____ because they are manufactured in make-shift laboratories and
   contain many impurities.

10. Most college students rely on _____ when they decide whether or not to use a drug.

11. A narcotic drug is any drug that has _____ as a main ingredient.

12. The drug most associated with violence, suicide, and accidental deaths is _____.

13. Those who use ecstasy can die from _____ and _____.

14. Those who use marijuana and are screened for drug use would be surprised to know that it is found _____ after one dose.

15. Adulterants, or substances used to "mask" drugs, are also _____ during drug testing.

16. _____ is a term used to describe a condition when an individual cannot go through one day or function "normally" without it.

17. The main ingredient to steroids is _____, which results in acceleration of male-like characteristics, acne, and aggression.

18. An individual with a legal blood alcohol concentration (BAC) who is driving can be _____ when they are driving and are stopped due to a traffic violation.

19. Children are most influenced by drug use of _____ more than any other type of influence.

20. Drug abuse is a _____ problem.

TAKE CHARGE WORKSHEET 7.4

Drug Actions and Interactions

DIRECTIONS: Define the following terms:

Tolerance =

Withdrawal =

Addiction =

DIRECTIONS: Draw a line from the type of drug category to the substance.

Drug Category	Substance
Narcotic (pain-killer)	Percocet
	Vicodin
	Codeine
	Hydrocodone
	Oxycotin
	Demerol
Depressant	Valium
	Rohypnol
	Special K
Stimulant	Crack
	Ephedra
	Caffeine
	Ecstasy
Hallucinogen	Marijuana
	Peyote
	Mushrooms
	LSD

DIRECTIONS: Draw a line to substances that should *not* be used together.

Birth control pills

St. John's Wort

Antibiotics (Ampicillin or Tetracycline)

Ginseng

Alcohol

Barbiturates (Xanax or Valium)

Anti-infective agents (Flagyl)

Cocaine

Antihistamines

Sunlight

Tetracycline

Retin A

Accutane

NAME: _____ DATE: _____

TAKE CHARGE WORKSHEET 7.5

Side Effect Alert

DIRECTIONS: All drugs have side effects and they effect each person differently according to the type of drug, dosage, frequency of use, and other behaviors of the user. Draw a line from the drug to its most frequently occurring side effect. Answers are located on the following page.

Substance	**Side Effect**
Caffeine	1. Increased urination and headaches with reduced dose or use.
Ephedra (Ma Huang)	
Androstendione	2. Dizziness, ringing in the ears, nervousness, tremors, high blood pressure, and cardiac arrhythmia.
Antihistamines	
Birth control pills	3. Irritability, acne on the arms and legs, enlarged clitoris, shrunken testicles, increased facial hair, and deepened voice.
Ecstasy (MDMA)	
Aspirin	4. Drowsiness and slow reaction time.
Anabolic steroids	5. Increased blood clotting, weight gain.
Decongestants	6. Increased body temperature, perspiration, dehydration, euphoria, and energy.
Diet pills	
Corticosteroids	7. Gastro-intestinal upset, blood thinning.
	8. Depletion of calcium stores in the body.

Answers

Substance	Side Effect
Caffeine	1
Ephedra (Ma Huang)	2
Androstendione	3
Antihistamines	4
Birth control pills	5
Ecstasy (MDMA)	6
Aspirin	7
Anabolic steroids	3
Decongestants	4
Diet pills	1
Corticosteroids	8

General Review Questions

1. Review the features of the six categories of drugs.

2. Discuss the routes by which drugs are administered.

3. What four symptoms are present in all addictions?

4. Explain how prescription drugs become over-the-counter drugs.

5. Explain how drugs are scheduled.

Practice Test 1

1. Michael is in college and drinks heavily at social events, but he doesn't believe that his drinking pattern is a problem. What is he experiencing?

   a. habit

   b. obsession

   c. compulsion

   d. denial

2. What is the most common route of administration of drugs?

   a. inhalation

   b. oral ingestion

   c. intravenous injection

   d. subcutaneous injection

3. Applying a small adhesive patch used to alleviate motion sickness introduces chemicals into the body through the skin. What is this route of administration?

   a. inhalation

   b. inunction

   c. subcutaneous injection

   d. oral administration

4. What form of drug administration transfers the drug rapidly into the bloodstream through the alveoli in the lungs?

   a. injection

   b. oral ingestion

   c. inunction

   d. inhalation

5. Addictions are characterized by all of the following symptoms, *except*
   a. loss of control.
   b. compulsion.
   c. awareness of self-destructive behavior.
   d. negative consequences.

6. Morphine, codeine, and heroin are all classified as:
   a. opiates.
   b. amphetamines.
   c. hallucinogens.
   d. designer drugs.

7. Prozac, Zoloft, and Paxil are among the most frequently prescribed:
   a. antibiotics.
   b. sedatives.
   c. antidepressants.
   d. tranquilizers.

8. Drugs that are marketed by their chemical names rather than a brand name are called:
   a. generic drugs.
   b. OTC drugs.
   c. recreational drugs.
   d. commercial drugs.

9. While Julie was taking antibiotics for strep throat, her doctor warned that taking antibiotics would make the birth control pills she was also taking less effective. This is an example of what type of drug interaction?
   a. antagonism
   b. inhibition
   c. synergism
   d. intolerance

10. Which of the following is *not* an effect of amphetamines?
    a. decreased heart rate
    b. appetite suppression
    c. insomnia
    d. restlessness

11. What is the active ingredient in marijuana?
    a. PCP
    b. MDMA
    c. LSD
    d. THC

12. Freebase is a form of:
    a. heroin.
    b. cocaine.
    c. amphetamines.
    d. marijuana.

13. Ecstasy is categorized as a:
    a. narcotic.
    b. depressant.
    c. hallucinogenic.
    d. designer drug.

14. Rubber cement, model glue, spot removers, and gasoline are examples of:
    a. depressants.
    b. inhalants.
    c. stimulants.
    d. psychedelics.

15. Cocaine, codeine, methadone, and morphine all fit under what drug schedule?
    a. Schedule I
    b. Schedule II
    c. Schedule III
    d. Schedule IV

Practice Test 2

1. A series of temporary physical and psychological symptoms that occur when the addict stops the addictive behavior is known as:

   a. addiction.

   b. withdrawal.

   c. tolerance.

   d. physiological dependence.

2. Antibiotics and vaccinations are normally administered by:

   a. intramuscular injection.

   b. inhalation.

   c. intravenous injection.

   d. suppositories.

3. What is the most frequently used illicit drug?

   a. LSD

   b. heroin

   c. cocaine

   d. marijuana

4. Rebecca takes a number of medications for various medical conditions, including Prinivil (an anti-hypertensive), insulin (a diabetic medication), and Claritin (an antihistamine). This is an example of:

   a. synergism.

   b. illegal drug use.

   c. polydrug use.

   d. antagonism.

5. When Sam developed a physiological tolerance to alcohol and showed a similar tolerance to barbiturates as a result, what had occurred?

   a. synergism

   b. antagonism

   c. cross-tolerance

   d. polydrug use

6. The type of interaction in which the effects of one drug are eliminated or reduced by the presence of another drug at the receptor site is called:

   a. antagonism.

   b. cross-tolerance.

   c. intolerance.

   d. inhibition.

7. Drugs that are used to relieve pain are classified as:

   a. analgesics.

   b. antibiotics.

   c. depressants.

   d. psychoactives.

8. It is spring and Roy is experiencing allergy symptoms, including a runny nose, sinus congestion, and tearing. When he goes to the store to buy an over-the-counter preparation, Roy should purchase a(n):

   a. decongestant.

   b. expectorant.

   c. antihistamine.

   d. antitussive.

9. A type of interaction in which two or more drugs produce extremely uncomfortable symptoms is called:

   a. antagonism.

   b. intolerance.

   c. inhibition.

   d. synergism.

10. What drug schedule has the lowest potential for abuse?

    a. Schedule I

    b. Schedule II

    c. Schedule IV

    d. Schedule V

11. Drugs with the highest potential for abuse and addiction are categorized as:

    a. Schedule I drugs.

    b. Schedule II drugs.

    c. Schedule III drugs.

    d. Schedule IV drugs.

12. The most common route of administration for heroin addicts is:

    a. inhalation.

    b. intravenous injection.

    c. ingestion.

    d. transdermal.

13. What hallucinogenic drug derives from the peyote cactus?

    a. mescaline

    b. methamphetamine

    c. LSD

    d. psilocybin

14. Synergism, antagonism, inhibition, and intolerance are:

    a. drug schedules.

    b. drug interactions.

    c. routes of drug administration.

    d. signs of addiction.

15. Juan is using the nicotine patch to help him quit smoking. What route of drug administration is he using?

    a. injection

    b. inunction

    c. inhalation

    d. suppository

8

Alcohol, Tobacco, and Caffeine

Chapter Overview

While caffeine, alcohol, and tobacco are considered legal drugs, this does not mean that they do not produce harmful effects on the body. All drugs affect mental and physical health. Alcohol is the most used and abused recreational drug. Many college students consume alcoholic beverages and one-third of all college students are considered heavy drinkers. A heavy drinker would be one who consumes alcohol on a regular basis or someone who consumes a large amount of alcohol whenever they do drink. A male binge drinker consumes five drinks in one sitting (1–5 hours) and a female binge drinker consumes four drinks in one sitting (1–5 hours). Binge drinking increases the risk of alcohol poisoning and death.

The effects of alcohol differ due to the amount of alcohol in each beverage. Fermented beverages such as beer and wine vary in alcohol content. Beers may be 2–6 percent alcohol, ales between 6–8 percent, and wines between 12–15 percent. The alcohol content of distilled beverages is much higher with 80 proof beverages having 40 percent alcohol and 100 proof beverages having 50 percent alcohol.

Blood alcohol concentration (BAC) is the ratio of alcohol to total blood volume. It is the factor used to measure the physiological and behavioral effects of alcohol. Despite individual differences, alcohol produces some general behavioral effects, depending on BAC. People can acquire physical and psychological tolerance to the effects of alcohol through regular use. The nervous system adapts over time, so greater amounts of alcohol are required to produce the same effects.

Several factors influence how quickly your body will absorb alcohol: the alcohol concentration in your drink, the amount of alcohol you consume, the amount of food in your stomach, pylorospasm, and your mood.

Alcohol is a diuretic, it depresses the central nervous system (CNS) and irritates the gastrointestinal system. Long-term effects of alcohol abuse include decreased intellectual ability, an increase in cardiovascular disease, liver disease, cancer, and birth defects. Fetal alcohol syndrome is a mental and physical disability developed in the fetus due to consumption of alcohol during pregnancy.

Drinking and driving increases the risk for motor vehicle fatalities and motor vehicle homicides. Whether the driver is under the legal BAC or not, driving is impaired and lives can be ruined.

When alcohol use interferes with work, school, social, or family relationships, or laws are violated, it becomes alcohol abuse or alcoholism. A person is more likely to become an alcoholic if members of their family were alcoholics. Stress, disappointments, relationship problems, and traumatic experiences increase the probability of alcohol abuse. Peer pressure increases the incidence of alcohol abuse among college students.

Treatment for alcoholism comes in the form of treatment centers, therapy, and Alcoholics Anonymous programs. Roughly 60 percent of alcoholics relapse within the first three months of treatment. This seemingly harmless drug can have lifelong effects for the user and the user's loved ones.

Tobacco use is the single most preventable cause of death in the United States. One in every five deaths in the United States is smoking related. The use of tobacco involves many social issues, including advertising targeted at youth and women, the largest-growing populations of smokers. Health care and lost productivity resulting from smoking cost the nation as much as $150 billion per year.

Tobacco can be consumed in the form of cigarettes, cigars, and smokeless products, all of which contain nicotine. Nicotine is a powerful drug that stimulates the central nervous system and causes addiction. Carbon monoxide is a poisonous by-product of burning cigarettes and there are many harmful chemicals in the tar. Cancer, cardiovascular disease, respiratory problems, sexual dysfunction, and gum disease are some of the harmful effects. In addition, nearly 9 out of 10 Americans are exposed to environmental tobacco smoke (ETS). People who breathe smoke from someone else's smoking product are said to be involuntary or passive smokers and face risks from ETS.

Quitting a tobacco habit is very difficult and a combination of methods is usually tried before there is success. Nicotine replacement (gum, patch, nasal spray, inhaler, and Zyban® pills) are effective, but most of these methods require a prescription. Other strategies include aversion therapy, operant conditioning, and using self-control techniques. There are numerous benefits of quitting. At the end of 10 smoke-free years, the ex-smoker can expect to live out his or her normal life-span.

Caffeine is a widely used central nervous system stimulant. Caffeine is a drug derived from the chemical family called xanthines. As the effects of caffeine wear off, users may feel let down. To counteract this, people commonly drink another cup of coffee, leading to tolerance and psychological dependence. Symptoms of caffeinism include chronic insomnia, jitters, irritability, nervousness, anxiety, and involuntary muscle twitches. Long-term caffeine use has been suspected of being linked to a number of health problems. However, no strong evidence exists to suggest that moderate caffeine use produces harmful effects in healthy, nonpregnant people.

NAME: _____ DATE: _____

TAKE CHARGE WORKSHEET 8.1

Are You Addicted?

DIRECTIONS: Many of us do not think that regular use of a substance is an indication of addiction. Place a checkmark in the column that most describes how frequently these things occur when you use caffeine, cigarettes, or alcohol. Indicate below which substance you are assessing.

Type of Substance: _____ Usual amount per use: _____

How frequently do you use the substance? _____ /day, _____ /week, or _____ /month

Question	Never	Sometimes	Frequently
Do you have urges or strong cravings to use this substance?			
Do you begin your day using it?			
If you have a limited amount of money to spend, do you use the money to buy it rather than something healthy?			
Do you experience withdrawal symptoms when you do not use it?			
How often do your friends use it?			
Have you ever had trouble remembering what you did when you were under the influence?			
Have you ever had a fight or an automobile accident when using it?			
Have you ever stolen anything so that you could get more of it or a substitute?			
Do you think that life is a pretty miserable experience without it? Have your friends or family members told you they were concerned about you?			
Do you spend more time under the influence than doing things that do not include substance use?			
Do you hide the fact that you use this substance from teachers, friends, or family members?			
Has use of this substance interfered with your obligations at school or at work?			
SCORE (number of checks in column)			

EVALUATION: If you had more checks in the column marked "never" than any other column, you are probably drug free or using the substance moderately. If you had more checks in any of the other columns, then the substance will cause or is causing problems that endanger your health and your life. Please consider changing this behavior.

NAME: _____ DATE: _____

TAKE CHARGE WORKSHEET 8.2

Caffeine Countdown

DIRECTIONS: Write in the space provided under each item below.

1. In order of "most caffeine" to "least caffeine," list the sources of caffeine in the correct order. The choices are: hot or cold chocolate milk, black tea, automatic drip coffee, carbonated citrus soft drinks, instant coffee, one chocolate candy bar, carbonated cola soft drinks, espresso drinks, green tea, decaffeinated coffee. Each drink would be 8 ounces.

   The product with the *most* caffeine is: _____ (most)

   _____

   _____

   _____

   _____

   _____

   _____

   _____

   _____

   _____ (least)

2. Write down the times of day and reasons why you are most likely consuming caffeine.

3. From the list below, check changes you have noticed since you began using caffeine.

   _____ more frequent urination

   _____ increased stomach upset

   _____ increased snacking

   _____ increased nervousness or anxiety

   _____ difficulty getting to sleep at night

   _____ irritability

   _____ other (write in) _____

4. Write at least five alternative foods and beverages that would help you reduce your caffeine consumption.

5. When you decide to decrease caffeine consumption, what time of day would be the best time to delay or eliminate caffeine consumption?

Answers

1. espresso drinks, automatic drip coffee, carbonated citrus soft drinks, instant coffee, carbonated cola soft drinks, black tea, chocolate bar, hot or cold chocolate milk, decaffeinated coffee, and green tea.

NAME: _____ DATE: _____

TAKE CHARGE WORKSHEET 8.3

A Dozen Drinking Dilemmas

DIRECTIONS: Imagine that you have found yourself in the situations described below. In the space provided, explain the best course of action to take to improve the situation.

1. You have several assignments to get done by the end of the week but your friends insist that you go out with them or you would "miss a good time." What could you do to get the assignments done and have a good time too?

2. A person who indicates they want to get to know you bought a drink and offers it to you. What should you do or say?

3. You wake up in the morning with a hangover. What should you do to prevent it from happening again?

4. When you wake up with a hangover, what is the best treatment?

5. You have a choice between drinking 12 ounces of beer, a 12 ounce glass of wine, or a mixed drink. Which one would have the least amount of alcohol in it?

6. You have had a few drinks and you have to drive home. What is the best action to take?

7. You want to lose weight and just learned that alcohol has "extra" calories. What can you drink when you are with friends at a party?

8. Your friend begins to act very strangely after drinking an alcoholic beverage. What should you do?

9. You have heard about binge drinking, but don't know if you are a binge drinker. How would you know?

10. You have a choice between a carbonated mixed drink and a beer. Which one is more likely to accelerate the effects? Which one would you chose?

11. You have a friend who has passed out due to drunkenness. What would be the best thing to do for them?

12. You are having a party and do not want to be responsible for any damages from fights or accidents. What could you do to make sure that your guests would be able to go home unharmed?

NAME: _____ DATE: _____

Smoke and Snuff Stumpers

DIRECTIONS: Write your best guess in the space provided.

1. Cigarette smoke has nicotine, tar, and carbon monoxide in it.

   Which of these is the "cancer-causing" substance?

   Which of these causes side effects in passive smokers?

   Which of these contributes to asthma, emphysema, and cancer?

2. Cigarette manufacturers have designed several different types of cigarettes like unfiltered, filtered, regular, menthol, longs, shorts, and low-tar.

   Which of these is more likely to burn faster?

   Which type would a smoker think irritates their lungs less?

   Which of these may have air holes in it so the smoker draws in air?

   Which of these is harmful to your health?

3. Cigarette smokers often have to pay higher health insurance premiums because they are more likely to be sick than non-smokers from pneumonia, bronchitis, lung cancer, emphysema, and viruses.

   Which of these is a beginning smoker most likely to have?

   Which of these is a smoker more likely to die from?

   Which of these is the most costly?

4. Some people think that chewing tobacco or snuff is a healthier alternative to smoking.

   Which of these is equivalent to 3–4 cigarettes?

   Which of these is a coarser cut?

5. Problems associated with using smokeless tobacco include esophageal cancer, gum disease, gastrointestinal problems, and cancer of the tongue.

   Which one is the smokeless tobacco user most likely to experience first?

   How often would a smokeless tobacco user have to use the product before they began to notice health problems?

NAME: _____ DATE: _____

TAKE CHARGE WORKSHEET 8.5

Passive Smoking

DIRECTIONS: Answer the following questions to assess your attitude toward and exposure to passive smoke. Describe your thoughts, feelings, or behavior in response to each question.

1. How many people in your home, apartment, or dorm room smoke?

2. Does your employer provide separate work/break areas for smokers and non-smokers?

3. Are smokers in your home or work environment considerate of non-smokers? If you smoke, are you considerate of non-smokers?

4. When I go to a restaurant with smokers (or with non-smokers and you are a smoker), I:

5. When I travel in a car with smokers (or with non-smokers and you are a smoker), I:

6. The things that bother me most about being around smokers are:

For Further Thought

Use these questions to initiate discussion with family, friends, employers, or co-workers about the effects of passive smoking and the rights of non-smokers.

NAME: _____ DATE: _____

TAKE CHARGE WORKSHEET 8.6

Beliefs About Smoking

DIRECTIONS: The statements below are about how you might be affected by smoking and how you gauge your belief in the negative effects of smoking. Circle whether you agree or disagree after each statement.

1. I would have to smoke regularly for many years before smoking would affect my health.

    Stongly Agree

    Agree

    Not Sure

    Disagree

    Strongly Disagree

2. Smoking only a few cigarettes a day would hurt my health.

    Stongly Agree

    Agree

    Not Sure

    Disagree

    Strongly Disagree

3. People who smoke are more successful than those who don't smoke.

    Stongly Agree

    Agree

    Not Sure

    Disagree

    Strongly Disagree

4. Pipes and cigars are safe to smoke if I don't inhale.

    Stongly Agree

    Agree

    Not Sure

    Disagree

    Strongly Disagree

5. After quitting, ex-smokers will be as healthy as if they had never smoked.

   Stongly Agree

   Agree

   Not Sure

   Disagree

   Strongly Disagree

6. The health risks of smoking can be overcome through exercise.

   Stongly Agree

   Agree

   Not Sure

   Disagree

   Strongly Disagree

7. Social gatherings are better when people are smoking.

   Stongly Agree

   Agree

   Not Sure

   Disagree

   Strongly Disagree

8. Smoking cigarettes is a sign of being mature.

   Stongly Agree

   Agree

   Not Sure

   Disagree

   Strongly Disagree

9. Most people who smoke cigarettes can quit smoking whenever they want to.

   Stongly Agree

   Agree

   Not Sure

   Disagree

   Strongly Disagree

General Review Questions

1. What factors influence how quickly you will absorb alcohol?

2. What are the long-term effects of alcohol consumption?

3. What are the symptoms of fetal alcohol syndrome?

4. What are the health hazards of smoking?

5. What are the addictive properties of caffeine?

Practice Test 1

1. At a BAC of 0.05, what behavioral effects does alcohol produce?

   a. relaxed mood

   b. motor impairment and a willingness to talk

   c. euphoric feelings and further motor impairment

   d. drowsiness sets in and motor impairment worsens, followed by a loss of judgment

2. Lindsay has joined a sorority, and when she goes to a social with a fraternity she usually has five or six drinks in a row. This type of high risk drinking is called:

   a. alcohol overconsumption.

   b. binge drinking.

   c. drinking overabuse.

   d. alcoholic addiction.

3. Doug likes to have a drink to help him feel slightly relaxed. The blood alcohol concentration level that produces this effect is:

   a. .02.

   b. .05.

   c. .08.

   d. .10.

4. At a party, Roger has been "shooting" tequila in large amounts over a short time. He has become unconscious and cannot be aroused. In addition, his breathing is irregular and his skin is bluish. Unless he gets immediate help, he can die from:

   a. alcohol abuse.

   b. pancreatitis.

   c. alcohol poisoning.

   d. delirium tremors.

5. Patrick was raised in an alcoholic family. To adapt to his father's alcoholic behavior, Patrick tried to divert attention from the problem by being too good to be true. What role did he assume?

   a. scapegoat

   b. family hero

   c. lost child

   d. mascot

6. The process by which addicts end their dependence on a drug and which is commonly carried out in a medical facility is called:

   a. recovery.

   b. intervention.

   c. detoxification.

   d. aversion therapy.

7. Alcohol is metabolized in the

   a. liver.

   b. kidneys.

   c. stomach.

   d. small intestine.

8. While smoking her first cigarette, Nancy begins to get dizzy, lightheaded, nauseated, and clammy skin. Nancy is most likely experiencing nicotine:

   a. poisoning.

   b. withdrawal.

   c. intolerance.

   d. overdose.

9. Nicotine acts as a(n) _____ on the central nervous system.

   a. stimulant

   b. analgesic

   c. depressant

   d. hallucinogenic

10. Paul's doctor prescribed Zyban® for him to help him quit:

    a. smoking cigarettes.

    b. smoking marijuana.

    c. drinking coffee.

    d. drinking alcohol.

11. What is the term for the chronic disease in which the alveoli are destroyed, making breathing difficult?

    a. stroke

    b. emphysema

    c. tachycardia

    d. chronic obstructive lung disorder

12. What percent of alcoholics relapse within the first three months of treatment?

    a. 20 percent

    b. 33 percent

    c. 50 percent

    d. 60 percent

13. How many years must an ex-smoker be smoke-free to expect to live out his or her normal life span?

    a. 2 years

    b. 5 years

    c. 10 years

    d. 15 years

14. Ed is an alcoholic who grew up with an alcoholic father. Alcohol was an accepted practice by both his parents and grandparents. In fact, his father took him out drinking to celebrate his 21st birthday. Ed is a

    a. Type I alcoholic.

    b. Type II alcoholic.

    c. Type III alcoholic.

    d. Type IV alcoholic.

15. A derivative of the chemical family of stimulants called xanthines is found in:

    a. snuff.

    b. nicotine.

    c. tobacco.

    d. coffee.

Practice Test 2

1. Children in dysfunctional families generally assume a specific role. Which role draws attention away from the family's primary problem through delinquency or misbehavior?

    a. family hero

    b. scapegoat

    c. lost child

    d. mascot

2. An effective method of helping an alcoholic to confront the disease is called:

    a. intermediary assistance.

    b. intervention.

    c. confrontation.

    d. reality orientation.

3. Blood alcohol concentration (BAC) is the:

    a. concentration of plant sugars in the blood stream.

    b. percentage of alcohol in a beverage.

    c. level of alcohol content in the blood before becoming drunk.

    d. ratio of alcohol to the total blood volume.

4. What is the most common form of tobacco use?

    a. smoking

    b. chewing

    c. sniffing

    d. snuffing

5. Greg has just quit smoking. When can he expect carbon monoxide levels in his blood to drop to normal and oxygen levels in his blood to increase to normal?

    a. 8 hours

    b. 24 hours

    c. 1 month

    d. 1 year

6. What percent of all traffic fatalities are alcohol-related?

    a. 10 percent

    b. 25 percent

    c. 40 percent

    d. 66 percent

7. A syndrome describing children with a history of prenatal alcohol exposure but without all of the physical or behavioral symptoms of fetal alcohol syndrome is:

   a. alcoholic behavioral syndrome.

   b. fetal alcoholic hepatitis.

   c. fetal alcohol effects.

   d. fetal alcoholic abuse.

8. Jane is a smoker and takes oral contraceptives. Because of this combination, she is at an increased risk for

   a. heart attack.

   b. infertility.

   c. amenorrhea.

   d. delayed menopause.

9. What is the most dangerous gas found in tobacco smoke?

   a. hydrogen cyanide

   b. carbon dioxide

   c. nitrogen dioxide

   d. carbon monoxide

10. The leading cause of cancer death from smoking is:

    a. throat cancer.

    b. colon cancer.

    c. lung cancer.

    d. stomach cancer.

11. Steve is working with a counselor to quit smoking. His counselor pairs the act of smoking with noxious stimuli, such as smoking rapidly. What technique is he using?

    a. aversion therapy

    b. operant conditioning

    c. nicotine withdrawal

    d. self-control therapy

12. Type 1 and Type 2 alcoholism support what causal factor in alcoholism?

    a. cultural

    b. learned

    c. social

    d. biological

13. The symptoms of chronic insomnia, jitters, irritability, anxiety, muscle twitches, and headaches describe

    a. caffeine overload.

    b. caffeine poisoning.

    c. theobromine syndrome.

    d. caffeinism.

14. Which of the following characterizes Type 1 alcoholics?

    a. avoids harmful situations

    b. lacks inhibition

    c. does not seek social approval

    d. prone to novelty-seeking behavior

15. Caffeine acts as a(n) _____ on the central nervous system.

    a. stimulant

    b. analgesic

    c. depressant

    d. hallucinogenic

9

Nutrition

Chapter Overview

Factors that influence dietary choices include personal preferences, habits, ethnic origin, social situations, availability, convenience, cost, emotions, values, body image concerns, and nutritional health concerns. Unfortunately, many Americans eat too many calories, especially from fatty foods. In spite of the trend in Americans to gain weight as they get older, weight should not increase with age. The Food Guide Pyramid was developed to help us select foods for a healthy diet. Vitamin and mineral supplements are not an adequate substitute for eating properly. Nutrient-dense foods such as fruits, vegetables, and grains are especially important. Alcohol, fats, sugar, and salt should be consumed in moderation, if not sparingly.

Essential nutrients are things our body needs to maintain overall good health. The most crucial essential nutrient is water. Carbohydrates are essential for growth and fuel. Carbohydrates come in two forms: simple sugars and complex carbohydrates. Complex carbohydrates are found in grains, cereals, vegetables, and fruits. Most of us do not get enough complex carbohydrates. Fiber also comes in two forms: soluble and insoluble. Soluble fiber is found in oats, beans, fruits, and vegetables and helps lower the risk for cardiovascular disease. Insoluble fiber found in whole grains, cereals, fruits, and vegetables helps prevent breast, colon, and rectal cancer. It may also prevent constipation, diverticulitis, diabetes, and obesity. While proteins are important, our body needs less protein than carbohydrates. Incomplete proteins from vegetable sources (e.g., beans, peas, peanuts, grains, nuts, and seeds) can be combined to create complete proteins. Complete proteins are also found in meat, eggs, and dairy products. Too much protein can strain the liver, kidneys, and kidney stones. Our body needs saturated fats (from meat and dairy products), monounsaturated fats (from vegetable products), and polyunsaturated fats (from oils). Hydrogenated vegetable fats (known as trans-fatty acids) are a concern because they may be just as harmful as saturated fats. Vitamins come in the form of water-soluble (B and C vitamins need to be included in our daily diet) and fat-soluble (A, D, E, and K are stored in the body). Minerals include macrominerals (sodium, calcium, phosphorus, magnesium, potassium, sulfur, and chloride) and trace minerals (iron, zinc, manganese, copper, iodine, and cobalt).

Men and women differ in body size, body composition, and overall metabolic rates. They therefore have differing needs for most nutrients throughout the life cycle. In addition, women have many more landmark times in life when their nutritional requirements vary significantly from requirements at other times, such as during pregnancy and lactation.

There are different types of diets in practice today. The most popular is the vegetarian diet, which has several variations. Some vegetarians include dairy products in their diets, some include eggs, some include fish, and some eat non-red meats. In general, a vegetarian diet is a healthy diet, but requires some creativity and planning to include all of the essential nutrients.

Food safety is a concern whether you are preparing foods at home, purchasing foods in the store, or traveling. College students often find it difficult to choose food wisely because of financial, time, and availability restraints. Nonetheless, eating a healthy diet is something that should not be left to chance. If you are conscious of your food selection and you purchase foods in advance, you can prepare healthier snacks and meals that will decrease your chances of ingesting harmful additives, having an allergic reaction, or obtaining a food-borne illness. Shelf life and food handling are also considerations in food safety.

NAME: _____ DATE: _____

TAKE CHARGE WORKSHEET 9.1

Are You Dehydrated?

Water is the most important nutrient we need. Without water, there would be no life. Dehydration is a serious problem. Lack of water creates other health problems.

DIRECTIONS: Record your water intake for three days using the table below. In the comments section, record observations about how you felt that day or other observations related to your consumption of water. Answer the following questions about water and determine whether or not you need to drink more water.

Date Recorded	Times	Total Ounces Consumed	Comments
Day One Date: _____	_____ _____ _____ _____		
Day Two Date: _____	_____ _____ _____ _____		
Day Three Date: _____	_____ _____ _____ _____		

1. How much water does the average person need?

2. How would you know if you were drinking enough water or fluids?

3. What types of drinks remove water stores in the body?

4. How does too much protein (from protein supplements and liquid protein diet drinks) in the diet contribute to dehydration?

5. How much water does an athlete need?

6. Is a sports drink better than water for athletes?

7. If you lose too much water through perspiration, vomiting, or diarrhea, do you need to drink beverages with electrolytes in them?

8. Is bottled water better for you than tap water?

9. Are sparkling waters just as good as regular water?

10. Does ice present a hazard when drinking water?

11. Why do we have chlorinated drinking water?

12. What ways could you add water to your diet or lifestyle?

Answers

1. The average person needs 6–8 eight ounce glasses per day. This is an average.

2. If you are drinking enough fluids, your urine will be a very light, yellow color.

3. Caffeinated and alcoholic drinks take water out of the body. That's why you go to the bathroom more often.

4. The body requires extra water to process excess protein intake so it can be excreted through urine. This is one reason why liquid protein diet drinks give a person the false impression that weight is lost. It is actually water that is lost. Individuals who have had excessive protein in their diets over a prolonged period of time may experience kidney stones because calcium stores are also drawn out of the body as it tries to process the excess protein.

5. Athletes always require more water because they perspire more and play in hot or humid environments. As sweat is lost, water must be replaced. Some athletes are weighed before and after a workout or event. The amount of weight lost determines how much water should be replaced. Rather than waiting until after an event, however, athletes need to drink before and during the practice or event to prevent dehydration.

6. Many people find it difficult to drink all the water they need. Sports drinks contain salt, which triggers a thirst response in the brain, and sweetened flavoring, which most individuals would drink more of than water. Children involved in youth sports should drink a sports drink rather than a fruit drink or a soft drink.

7. Excessive sweating will remove sodium from the body. Vomiting and diarrhea remove potassium from the body. Sports drinks usually contain both of these electrolytes and would be beneficial so that other complications such as muscle exhaustion, muscle cramping, and inability to retain food would be lessened.

8. Unless the bottle says purified, which means it was boiled and the steam condensed into liquid form again, most bottled waters *are* nothing but tap water.

9. Anything carbonated has carbon dioxide in it. Drinking a carbonated beverage of any type will increase carbon dioxide levels in the blood, making us tired and gassy.

10. In places where water purity is a concern, such as a "greasy spoon" restaurant or a foreign country, the water may be fine, but the ice may have harmful bacteria. If you doubt the cleanliness of the icemaker or the cooler where ice is stored, you may be better off drinking water without the ice.

11. In a municipal water system, there is always the danger of cross contamination from sewer systems and the water management process. Water is always monitored for *E. coli* bacteria. In order for *E. coli* and other bacteria to be eliminated or less harmful to an individual, chlorine is added to the water supply.

12. Ways to increase water include ordering water with meals rather than other beverages, drinking water mid-morning or mid-afternoon, drinking milk, or fruit juices, drinking fewer caffeinated drinks, and drinking fewer alcoholic drinks.

NAME: _____ DATE: _____

TAKE CHARGE WORKSHEET 9.2

Food Log

DIRECTIONS: Rather than writing down everything you eat (which can be time consuming), record the number of servings you eat each day, using the table below as a guide. Portion sizes are important. Use the serving sizes below to help you determine the portion size. If you eat 6 ounces of meat, for example, knowing a serving is 3 ounces, you would write 2 servings in the table. If the meat were hamburger or steak, which contains extra fat, mark down the amount of extra fat in that column.

Serving Sizes

Milk = 8 oz. skim milk, $1\frac{1}{2}$ cup ice cream or pudding, 1 cup yogurt, 1–1.5 oz. of cheese

Meat = 3 oz., one hotdog, 2 strips of bacon, 1 sausage

Fruits = small apple, orange, or banana, or $\frac{1}{2}$ cup canned or raw

Vegetables = $\frac{3}{4}$ cup of cooked or canned, 1 cup of lettuce

Grains = 1 slice of bread, $\frac{1}{2}$ bun, $\frac{1}{2}$ bagel, $\frac{1}{2}$ English muffin, 6–10 crackers, 3 cups of popcorn, $\frac{1}{2}$ cup of cooked cereal, 1 cup of dry cereal

Sugar = 1 teaspoon

Fat = 1 teas. to 1 Tbsp. in mayonnaise, dressings

 = 1 teas. butter, margarine, cream cheese

Your Serving Sizes

Date and Day of the Week	Servings of Milk	Servings of Meat	Servings of Fruit	Servings of Vegetables	Servings of Grains	Extra Sugar	Extra Fat

Recommended Serving Sizes

According to the food guide pyramid, the required amounts from each food group are:

Milk = 2 servings

Meat = 2 servings (or 6 oz.)

Fruits = 2–3 servings

Vegetables = 3–4 servings

Cereals = 6–11 servings

Fat = some fat is necessary, but let's not overdo it

Sugar = as little as possible

EVALUATION: Below make two columns, one marked *Increase* and one marked *Decrease*. List the food groups you need to increase and decrease for a balanced diet in the appropriate column.

NAME: _____ DATE: _____

TAKE CHARGE WORKSHEET 9.3

Are You Nutrient Dense?

DIRECTIONS: Answer the questions below in the space provided. Compare your answers with those in the Answer section.

1. How many calories does a young female adult need?

2. How many calories does a young male adult need?

3. Which types of calorie sources from food have the most calories per gram?

4. How much of your diet (total calories consumed) should consist of carbohydrates?

5. Which food groups contain carbohydrates?

6. What is the basis for including simple carbohydrates in the body?

7. Which types of foods contain simple carbohydrates?

8. What is the basis for including complex carbohydrates in the body?

9. Which types of food contain complex carbohydrates?

10. What does the term "nutrient dense" mean?

11. Are there different types of fiber?

12. If I'm eating all the right foods, why is it that I'm still gaining weight?

13. Wouldn't it just be simpler to take a vitamin and mineral supplement?

14. Don't females require some vitamin and mineral supplements?

15. If I were going to restrict my caloric intake so I could lose weight, how low can I limit my calories without starving myself?

16. How can I gain weight and add muscle?

Answers

1. Calorie requirements vary according to height, gender, and amount of physical activity. A sedentary female needs about 2000 calories. If she is physically active, extra calories are needed.

2. Males have higher metabolisms than females and can eat more calories without gaining weight. A sedentary male needs about 2500 calories. The taller and more active the male, the more calories he can eat.

3. Fat has the highest with 9 calories per gram. Alcohol has 7 calories per gram. Carbohydrates and protein have 4 calories per gram. A calorie is a unit of measurement used to describe how much energy is required for your body to use each gram as fuel.

4. Approximately 52–58% of our diet should consist of carbohydrates. That would be about 1040–1160 calories for females and 1300–1450 calories for males. About 10% of these should come from simple sugars (100–110 calories for females, 130–145 calories for males) and the rest should come from complex carbohydrates.

5. All foods contain carbohydrates unless they are 100% fat like oils, margarine, or butter.

6. Simple carbohydrates provide quick energy sources for fuel from glucose, sucrose, fructose, lactose, galactose, and other simple forms.

7. Table sugar, fruit drinks, sports drinks, fruit juices, skim milk, and candies all have easily digestible sugars.

8. Complex carbohydrates contain vitamins, minerals, and fiber that are not found in simple sugar sources.

9. Fruits, vegetables, and grains contain complex carbohydrates. When an endurance athlete uses "carbohydrate loading" prior to a major event, it includes large amounts of pasta, rice, bread, fruits, and vegetables.

10. Nutrient dense means that you get more nutrients per ounce than other food sources. Raw fruits and vegetables are more nutrient dense than cooked foods because they usually have more fiber. Some foods are fortified or enriched to improve nutrient density.

11. There are two types of fiber: soluble and insoluble. Soluble fiber is found in fruits, vegetables, and beans. It has health-enhancing properties by lowering risk of hypertension, stroke, high cholesterol, heart attacks, breast cancer, and colon cancer. Insoluble fiber is needed so food moves through the intestinal tract. Sources of insoluble fiber include grains and nuts.

12. The main reason why we gain weight even if we are eating a balanced diet is because we need more activity to balance the calories consumed and expended. Another reason for weight gain could be a change in hormones from pregnancy, birth control pills, or Depo-Provera shots. Lots of foods also contain "hidden calories" because they are higher in fat and sugar than we think. Uncontrolled portion sizes often sneak up on the calorie count.

13. You could take a vitamin and mineral supplement, but it doesn't add fiber if we are dependent on fast, convenience, or processed foods. There are two types of vitamins: water-soluble and fat-soluble. Water soluble vitamins are needed by the body every day but if we take too much of them, they are just excreted in the urine. Fat-soluble vitamins are stored in the body and too much of them can cause serious problems. Since we need calories from foods anyway, taking a vitamin supplement just helps us continue eating foods high in sugar and fat, which contribute to obesity problems.

14. Some females do. Women who are lactose intolerant need a calcium supplement. Women who have heavy menstrual periods or intense workouts need more iron. Women taking birth control pills or who have problems with PMS need more B vitamins.

15. Females should eat at least 1200 calories per day and males should eat at least 1500 calories per day. This doesn't seem like much, but if you buy a lean TV dinner containing only 300 calories, you could have 3–5 of these per day.

16. Extra carbohydrates, protein, and fats add calories. Add two extra snacks per day and maintain your current activity level and you will see a gain in weight. Include weight lifting with your increase in calories and you will see an increase in muscle. As you become less active, however, you will need fewer calories.

TAKE CHARGE WORKSHEET 9.4

Food Poisoning Prevention

DIRECTIONS: Answer the questions below to see if you know how to prevent a case of food poisoning. Compare your answers with those in the Answer section.

1. Most causes of food poisoning are from:

    a. eating in a cafeteria.

    b. eating in a restaurant.

    c. eating at a picnic.

    d. eating at home.

2. Which of the following is more likely to cause a case of salmonella?

    a. Chicken that has not been cooked long enough

    b. Eating or drinking something with raw eggs in it

    c. Using a cracked egg

    d. All of the above

3. The most common cause of food poisoning is from:

    a. cross-contamination of different foods on the same cutting board.

    b. lack of proper hand washing.

    c. eating uncooked shellfish.

    d. eating spoiled food.

4. What is the best temperature for your refrigerator?

    a. 20–31°F

    b. 32–40°F

    c. 41–50°F

    d. 51–60°F

5. The best method for defrosting meats is:

    a. to thaw it in the refrigerator overnight.

    b. to defrost it in the microwave before cooking.

    c. to leave it in the sink or on the counter for several hours.

    d. none of the above

6. What is the best method of cooking to be sure hamburger is safe from bacteria?

    a. Rare

    b. Medium rare

    c. Medium

    d. Medium well

7. How long should you wash your hands with soap and water before cooking?

    a. 5 seconds

    b. 10 seconds

    c. 15 seconds

    d. 30 seconds

8. In order to sanitize dishes and glasses, the temperature of dishwasher water should be:

    a. 150°F.

    b. 120°F.

    c. 100°F.

    d. 80°F.

NAME: _____ DATE: _____

TAKE CHARGE WORKSHEET 9.5

Grocery Shopping List

DIRECTIONS: Many people get in a "rut" and buy the same foods each time, forgetting to shop for foods they enjoy. Circle all the items in the list below that you like and make plans to get some of those items the next time you go to the store. If you haven't tried some of these items, you might want to try them.

Fruits

Apples, apricots, bananas, blueberries, cantaloupe, cherries, dates, dried apricots, grapefruit, grapes, honeydew melon, kiwi fruit, mango, oranges, papaya, peaches, pears, persimmon, pineapples, plums, raisins, starfruit (carambola), strawberries, tangerines, tomatoes, watermelon.

Vegetables

Asparagus, bamboo shoots, beets, broccoli, Brussel sprouts, cabbage, carrots, cauliflower, celery, chard, corn, cucumber, eggplant, fresh parsley, garlic, green beans, potatoes, snow peas, spinach, summer squash, green peppers, red peppers, sweet potatoes, turnips, watercress, winter squash.

Beverages

Cocoa, coffee, fruit juice, vegetable juice, tea, seltzer, ginger ale.

Snack Foods

Cookies, granola bars, popcorn, baked potato chips, pretzels, baked tortilla chips.

Canned Goods

Applesauce, beets, broth, corn, cranberry sauce, evaporated skim milk, fruit (in juice), peanut butter, peas, soup, tomatoes, tomato sauce, tomato paste, tuna (water-packed).

Baking Ingredients

Baking powder, baking soda, cocoa powder, cornstarch, flavorings, whole wheat flour, enriched flour, spices, herbs, sugar, nuts.

Legumes

Canned beans, dried beans or peas, tofu, soy products.

Condiments

Jam, jelly, ketchup, low-fat mayonnaise, mustard, salad dressing, salsa, soy sauce, oil, vinegar.

Meats

Beef, chicken, fish, ground beef, ground turkey, turkey breast, ham, lamb, pork, shellfish, turkey, veal.

Frozen Foods

Bread dough, dinners, frozen yogurt, ice cream, sorbet.

Dairy Products

Butter, mozzarella cheese, cheddar cheese, cream cheese, Neufchatel cheese, dips, eggs, margarine, milk, nonfat dry milk, sour cream, yogurt.

Grain Products

Bagels, whole grain bread, enriched bread, bulgur, couscous, oatmeal, ready-to-eat whole grain cereal, crackers, English muffins, noodles, pasta, pita bread, brown rice, enriched rice, whole grain rolls, tortillas.

NAME: _____ DATE: _____

TAKE CHARGE WORKSHEET 9.6

Your Eating Habits and Extra Calories

DIRECTIONS: Think about your eating patterns and habits: what, how much, when, where, and why you eat. For each of these questions, check the answers that best describe your eating patterns and habits.

What Do I Usually Eat?

_____ A varied and balanced diet that includes only moderate amounts of fat and alcoholic beverages.

_____ Deep-fat, fried, and breaded foods.

_____ Extras, such as salad dressings, potato toppings, spreads, sauces, and gravies.

_____ Sweets and rich desserts such as candies, cakes, and pies.

_____ Snack foods high in fat and sodium, such as chips and other "munchies."

_____ Cocktails, wine, and beer.

How Much Do I Usually Eat?

_____ A single, small serving.

_____ A large serving.

_____ Two servings or more.

When Do I Usually Eat?

_____ At mealtime only.

_____ While preparing meals or clearing the table.

_____ At coffee break.

_____ Anytime.

Where Do I Usually Eat?

_____ At the kitchen or dining room table.

_____ At restaurants or fast food places.

_____ In front of the TV or while reading.

_____ Wherever I happen to be when I'm hungry.

Why Do I Usually Eat?

_____ It's time to eat.

_____ I'm starved.

_____ Foods look tempting.

_____ Everyone else is eating.

_____ Food will get thrown away if I don't eat it.

_____ I'm bored or frustrated.

EVALUATION: Look at the boxes you checked for "what" and "how much" you eat. Do they provide any clues to where your extra calories are coming from? Your answers to "when, where, and why" you eat are important, too. They often affect what and how much you eat.

Can you identify some habits that may be due for a change? Try to think of ways to modify "problem" habits. If, for example, you often nibble while doing other things, make an effort to plan your meals and snacks ahead of time. For eating at home, make a rule to eat only while sitting at the kitchen or dining room table. If candy bars from the vending machine at your office coffee break are a problem, substitute a low-calorie snack brought from home. If you often eat because you're bored or frustrated, think of other activities to get your mind off food, like jogging, calling a friend, or walking the dog.

General Review Questions

1. What factors influence our eating behaviors?

2. What food groups are under the Food Guide Pyramid and what are the recommended servings for each?

3. What are the benefits of fiber?

4. Distinguish between low-density lipoproteins (LDLs) and high-density lipoproteins (HDLs).

5. Why can men eat more than women without gaining weight?

Practice Test 1

1. Americans typically get most of their calories from:

    a. fat.

    b. proteins.

    c. simple sugars.

    d. complex carbohydrates.

2. What nutrient aids in fluid and electrolyte balance, maintains pH balance, and transports molecules and cells throughout the body?

    a. water

    b. minerals

    c. vitamins

    d. fat

3. What substances are made up of amino acids that are major components of cells?

    a. vitamins

    b. carbohydrates

    c. proteins

    d. minerals

4. What type of carbohydrates are primarily found in grains, cereals, dark green leafy vegetables, and cruciferous vegetables?

    a. glucose

    b. dextrose

    c. simple carbohydrates

    d. complex carbohydrates

5. What nutrient supplies us with the energy needed to sustain normal daily activity?

   a. protein

   b. fats

   c. carbohydrates

   d. fiber

6. What is the best way to increase dietary fiber in a diet?

   a. Eat more meat.

   b. Eat more complex carbohydrates.

   c. Decrease the amount of water to 3–4 glasses per day.

   d. Decrease the amount of fruit while increasing beans and nuts.

7. Nutritionists recommend that fats make up no more than what percent of our total diet?

   a. 10 percent

   b. 20 percent

   c. 30 percent

   d. 40 percent

8. Dehydration is a result of lack of

   a. sodium.

   b. water.

   c. protein.

   d. carbohydrates.

9. The Food Guide Pyramid recommends how many daily servings of fruit?

   a. 2–4

   b. 3–5

   c. 5–7

   d. 6–11

10. Ron consumes large quantities of vitamin supplements. His doctor warned him that overusing vitamins can lead to a toxic condition known as:

    a. toxoplasmosis.

    b. hemochromatosis.

    c. hypervitaminosis.

    d. intolerance.

11. What major organ determines whether nutrients are stored, sent to cells or organs, or excreted?

    a. liver

    b. kidneys

    c. stomach

    d. pancreas

12. What are two major forms of complex carbohydrates?

    a. glucose and fructose

    b. starches and fiber

    c. complete proteins and incomplete proteins

    d. saturated fats and unsaturated fats

13. What is the most common nutrient deficiency worldwide?

    a. fat deficiency

    b. iron deficiency

    c. fiber deficiency

    d. calcium deficiency

14. What nutrient plays a vital role in the maintenance of healthy skin and hair, insulation of the body organs against shock, maintenance of body temperature, and the proper functioning of the cells themselves?

    a. fats

    b. fiber

    c. protein

    d. carbohydrates

15. What is a common cause of anemia?

    a. ulcers

    b. cancers

    c. accidents

    d. iron deficiency

Practice Test 2

1. Carrie eats fish, dairy products, and eggs, but does not eat red meat. Carrie is considered a(n):

    a. vegan.

    b. lacto-vegetarian.

    c. ova-vegetarian.

    d. pesco-vegetarian.

2. Amino acids that must be obtained from food are referred to as:

    a. nonessential amino acids.

    b. essential amino acids.

    c. complete amino acids.

    d. incomplete amino acids.

3. Which of the following nutrients does *not* contribute any calories to our diets?

    a. fats

    b. minerals

    c. proteins

    d. carbohydrates

4. Oat bran and dried beans are major sources of:

    a. alpha cellulose.

    b. triglycerides.

    c. soluble fiber.

    d. insoluble fiber.

5. What is the most common form of fat in the body?

    a. cholesterol

    b. triglyceride

    c. saturated fat

    d. unsaturated fat

6. What is a major cause of atherosclerosis?

    a. plaque

    b. high density lipoproteins

    c. unsaturated fats

    d. monounsaturated fats

7. Folate is a type of vitamin _____ that is believed to decrease levels of homocysteine, an amino acid that has been linked to vascular diseases.

    a. A

    b. B

    c. E

    d. K

8. William does not have the digestive chemicals needed to break down the lactose in milk. This is an example of:

    a. food allergy.

    b. food poisoning.

    c. food intolerance.

    d. indigestion.

9. What is the most common form of simple sugar in our diet?

    a. glucose

    b. sucrose

    c. fructose

    d. lactose

10. What percentage of our total body weight is water?

    a. 15 to 20 percent

    b. 30 to 40 percent

    c. 50 to 60 percent

    d. 70 to 75 percent

11. Which of the following nutrients moves food through the digestive tract?

    a. fat

    b. fiber

    c. minerals

    d. starch

12. What is the most crucial nutrient?

    a. water

    b. fiber

    c. protein

    d. carbohydrates

13. What substance supplies us with the energy needed to sustain normal daily activity?

    a. fats

    b. fibers

    c. proteins

    d. carbohydrates

14. What substance plays a vital role in maintaining healthy skin and hair, insulating body organs against shock, maintaining body temperature, and promoting healthy cell function?

    a. fats

    b. fibers

    c. proteins

    d. carbohydrates

15. Which of the following is a trace mineral?

    a. zinc

    b. sodium

    c. calcium

    d. phosphorus

10

Managing Your Weight

Chapter Overview

Sixty-one percent of American adults are either overweight or obese—an increase of more than 5 percent over the past decade. Obesity is a major problem with serious health consequences that amount to billions of dollars in medical expenses and lost income in the United States, and rivals smoking as a cause of preventable death.

Experts disagree as to what "normal" body fat composition is, but women are expected to have more body fat than men. For both genders, some fat is essential for normal nerve conduction and hormone regulation and other physiological functions. Additional body fat is considered storage fat and some of this fat is necessary to cushion the body and its vital organs. Excessively low levels of body fat in women disrupt the menstrual cycle. There are several methods for measuring body fat, including hydrostatic weighing techniques, pinch and skinfold measures, girth and circumference measures, soft-tissue roentgenogram, bioelectrical impedance analysis, and total body electrical conductivity. The body mass index (BMI) is used to determine the average normal weight in individual adults.

Each person's ideal body weight depends on factors such as gender, height, body structure, and weight distribution. Unfortunately, height and weight tables for average individuals do not take into account athletes, who weigh more but have higher percentages of lean muscle.

Advertising, eating out more, heredity, development during childhood, uncontrolled appetite, lifestyle, metabolic changes, or hormone imbalance are reasons for obesity. Losing weight and controlling weight after a desired weight is achieved is a lifelong process for many Americans. Setting realistic goals, seeking support from others, changing food purchases, eating habits, and increasing physical activity are all needed to maintain the behavior change. Increasing physical activity will increase metabolic rate and help the body expend more calories.

Fasting, low calorie diets, and starvation diets cause significant health risks. Weight is lost rapidly because of water and protein loss. Side effects of these diets include decreased blood sugar, cold tolerance, constipation, dehydration, diarrhea, emotional problems, fatigue, headaches, heart irregularity, ketosis, kidney infections, loss of lean body tissue, decreased metabolic rate, and weakness. Such diets should be used only when prescribed and supervised by a physician.

Another danger to such extreme methods is called the "yo-yo" effect as weight is gained, lost, regained, and lost many times over.

Many people have problematic eating behaviors which are triggered by environmental factors. Both genders can suffer from eating disorders, but they are most common among women. Binge eating, anorexia nervosa, bulimia nervosa, and excessive exercise are all forms of eating disorders. Each of these eating disorders requires medical and clinical therapy intervention.

NAME: _____ DATE: _____

TAKE CHARGE WORKSHEET 10.1

How Much Should You Weigh?

DIRECTIONS: Using a scale, weigh yourself without shoes.

Your current height: _____   Your current weight: _____

DIRECTIONS: Using the Healthy Weight Table below, determine what a healthy weight for you would be (the table applies to men and women).

Healthy Weight Table

Female		Male	
Height	Weight	Height	Weight
4'10"	91–119	5'9"	129–169
4'11"	94–124	5'10"	132–174
5'0"	97–128	5'11"	136–172
5'1"	101–132	6'0"	140–184
5'2"	104–137	6'1"	144–189
5'3"	107–141	6'2"	152–200
5'5"	114–150	6'3"	152–200
5'6"	118–155	6'4"	156–205
5'7"	121–160	6'5"	160–211
5'8"	125–164	6'6"	164–216

DIRECTIONS: Using a tape measure, determine your waist size, hip size, and waist-to-hip ratio (WHR). For waist size, measure around the smallest part of the waist. For hip size, measure around the largest part of the hips and buttocks. To calculate WHR, divide the waist size by the hip size.

Waist size: _____ Hip size: _____ WHR: _____

If your WHR is .80 for women or .90 for men, you have higher cardiovascular disease risk.

A waistline over 35 inches for women and over 40 inches for men indicates greater health risk.

DIRECTIONS: Use the following formula from your textbook, calculate your body mass index (BMI).

Multiply weight in pounds by 700 _____ x 700 = _____

Convert height to inches = _____ inches

Divide weight by height^2 _____ ÷ _____ = _____

Desirable BMI is 18.5–24.9 kg/m^2 for both men and women.

If you have had a weight problem since childhood, it will be more difficult to lose weight than someone who has recently gained weight. WHR ratio indicates cardiovascular risk. Studies have shown that many individuals who have had heart attacks have carried their weight in the waist and abdominal area. There is no ideal method for determining ideal body weight, but you can use the Healthy Weight Ranges from Table 10.1 on page 259 of your textbook.

NAME: _____ DATE: _____

TAKE CHARGE WORKSHEET 10.2

It Doesn't Last If You Fast

Anyone who wants to lose weight will usually want it to happen quickly. The problem is, if weight is lost quickly, it will also return quickly. The best weight loss goal is to one to two pounds per week.

DIRECTIONS: Write in the number of pounds you wish to lose and how long it would take to lose that weight gradually.

I would like to lose _____. This will probably take _____.

While fasting (eating nothing or very little besides fluids) is considered "cleansing" by some weight loss advocates, it is not very effective over a long period of time. The problem with dieting (limiting caloric intake by avoiding foods you enjoy) is that you feel deprived and sooner or later, you will go back to your pre-diet eating habits.

DIRECTIONS: If you plan to change eating habits to gradually decrease weight, check the suggestions below that you might want to try.

_____ Put food in cupboards or places where it is out of sight to reduce snacking.

_____ On the weekend, purchase enough fresh fruits/vegetables and whole grain breads to last one week.

_____ Carry healthy snacks and fruit juices in your back pack rather than resorting to vending machines or fast food restaurants.

_____ Purchase non-fat milk and low-fat salad dressings.

_____ Use a smaller plate so you will put less food on it.

_____ Keep portions of high-calorie foods like biscuits/gravy, cheesecake, or ice cream small ($1/2$ cup or one scoop or a thin slice).

_____ Do not eat in front of the television where you will forget how much you have eaten.

_____ Slow down when you eat.

_____ Avoid buffet, cafeteria, pot-luck dinners, or family-style eating where you are likely to sample everything or go back for seconds.

_____ Order water with your meal instead of alcohol or soft drinks.

_____ Drink water or have a clear soup before the main meal comes so you will feel full sooner.

_____ When you order from a menu, select foods that are not fried.

_____ When you feel full, ask the waiter for a take home box so you can enjoy the meal again the next day, rather than stuff yourself.

_____ Limit caloric intake Monday through Friday, then reward yourself on the weekend with something you enjoy eating.

DIRECTIONS: Indicate below when you intend to start modifying some of your eating habits using the techniques above.

I plan to change my eating habits _____ in order to reach my goal
(date)

by _____ .
(date)

NAME: _____ DATE: _____

TAKE CHARGE WORKSHEET 10.3

Exercising to Lose Weight

DIRECTIONS: Indicate any problems you might have that would interfere with certain physical activities. Write in any others that are not on the list.

_____ cardiac problems

_____ respiratory problems

_____ neck and spinal problems

_____ shoulder problems

_____ elbow problems

_____ lower back problems

_____ hip or knee problems

_____ ankle or foot problems

Other _____

DIRECTIONS: When increasing physical activity to lose weight, the amount of time exercising is more important than the intensity. Select the type of exercise you would enjoy doing daily. Write in any other activities not on this list.

_____ walking briskly   _____ jogging or running

_____ riding a bicycle outdoors   _____ riding a stationary bicycle

_____ lap swimming   _____ weight training

_____ playing golf   _____ playing softball

_____ playing basketball   _____ playing soccer or rugby

                                                  Other _____

DIRECTIONS: Determine when the best time of the day to exercise would be for you. You do not have to exercise continuously (although that would be the best), you may exercise 10–15 minutes at a time several times throughout the day. If you have a job where you are required to be on your feet and you are still overweight, you still need additional exercise.

I plan to exercise _____ (when) _____ (where) each day.

DIRECTIONS: Set a daily exercise goal that you would be able to achieve in one week. For example, "I plan to exercise by walking 20 minutes per day for a total of 140 minutes per week."

I plan to exercise by _____ (activity) for _____ minutes per day for a total of _____ minutes per week.

DIRECTIONS: Set a reward that you are willing to work to receive. Do not reward yourself if you do not achieve your weekly goal. Once you have achieved this goal, set your goal a little higher by increasing the number of minutes the next week.

If I achieve my weekly goal, I will reward myself on the weekend by _____ .

NAME: _____ DATE: _____

TAKE CHARGE WORKSHEET 10.4

Risks for Developing an Eating Disorder: Assessing Your Eating Behaviors

DIRECTIONS: Answer the following questions to assess your risk for developing an eating disorder.

1. Is your body weight below a minimally normal weight for your age and height?

2. Have people ever told you that you are too thin or have lost too much weight?

3. Are you afraid of gaining weight or becoming fat?

4. Do parts of your body "feel" fat, even though you are underweight?

5. Does your body weight or body shape influence how you feel about yourself?

6. Are other people concerned about your low weight?

7. Are you concerned about the physical effects of your low weight?

8. Are your menstrual periods irregular or absent?

9. Do you binge eat, that is, eat a larger amount of food that most people would eat, in a short period of time?

10. During a binge, do you feel you lose control of your eating?

11. Are you distressed about your binge eating?

12. To prevent weight gain from the binge, do you purge, that is, vomit, go on strict diets afterwards, fast, use laxatives, use diet pills, use water pills, give yourself an enema, or exercise vigorously?

If you answered yes to any of these questions, you may be at risk for anorexia nervosa, binge eating disorder, or bulimia nervosa. Professional help is available. Contact your physician or your college student counseling office to locate a psychotherapist who specializes in the treatment of eating disorders.

For Further Thought

Go to the following websites for more information on eating disorders:

http://www.edap.org/
National Eating Disorders Association

http://www.something-fishy.org/
The Something Fishy Website on Eating Disorders

http://www.edreferral.com/
Eating Disorder Referral and Information Center

http://www.anred.com/
Anorexia Nervosa and Related Eating Disorders, Inc.

NAME: _____ DATE: _____

Why Do You Eat?

DIRECTIONS: Determine how you feel about eating while examining your eating habits by checking the appropriate boxes below.

Situation	Always	Frequently	Occasionally	Seldom	Never
I eat to stimulate myself to stay awake.					
I eat for pleasure.					
I eat when I'm angry about something.					
I enjoy eating my favorite snack foods.					
I eat without realizing how much I ate.					
I eat because I enjoy preparing food.					
I eat to relax.					
I eat when I'm uncomfortable or anxious about something.					
I get uncomfortable when I am not eating.					
I eat because I feel better after I eat.					
If I'm sad or depressed, I eat.					
I eat because I'm hungry.					
I eat because I have stomach pangs.					
Sometimes I find myself eating without realizing I am putting something in my mouth.					

For Further Thought

In order to control your eating habits, you might want to analyze some of the reasons why you eat excessively. Some reasons could be increased energy/stimulation, satisfaction when handling foods, pleasurable sensations associated with eating, cravings, and habit. Determine what your problematic eating behaviors are and develop a plan for changing these habits.

General Review Questions

1. Distinguish between overweight and obesity. What percent of Americans are overweight or obese?

2. What are ways to measure body fat?

3. Using the Body Mass Index (BMI), what are healthy weights for males and females?

4. What is a calorie?

5. Explain setpoint theory.

Practice Test 1

1. What percent of persons who are obese are identified as *mildly obese*?

   a. 7 percent

   b. 20 percent

   c. 65 percent

   d. 90 percent

2. The ratio of lean body mass to fat body mass is called:

   a. obesity.

   b. body composition.

   c. overweight mass ratio.

   d. obesity ratio.

3. The technique of body fat assessment in which electrical currents are passed through fat and lean tissue is called:

   a. body mass index.

   b. hydrostatic weight technique.

   c. bioelectrical impedance analysis.

   d. soft-tissue roentgenogram.

4. What is the ideal total body fat for women?

   a. 11–15 percent

   b. 18–22 percent

   c. 23–29 percent

   d. 27–35 percent

5. Essential fat makes up approximately _____ percent of total body weight in men and approximately _____ percent of total body weight in women.

   a. 3 to 5; 18
   b. 3 to 7; 15
   c. 5 to 25; 13
   d. 3 to 5; 7

6. What part of the brain regulates appetite and closely monitors levels of certain nutrients in the blood?

   a. pituitary gland
   b. hypothalamus
   c. thyroid gland
   d. cerebellum

7. A person who is 70 percent above their ideal weight is described as

   a. mildly obese.
   b. moderately obese.
   c. severely obese.
   d. morbidly obese.

8. Melanie suffers from an acute form of self-starvation motivated by a fear of gaining weight and a severe disturbance in the perception of her body. She suffers from:

   a. anorexia nervosa.
   b. bulimia nervosa.
   c. binge eating disorder.
   d. compulsive eating disorder.

9. A condition in which the body adapts to prolonged fasting or carbohydrate deprivation by converting body fat to ketones, which can be used as fuel for some brain cells, is called

   a. caloric adaptation.
   b. carbohydrate synthesis.
   c. acidosis.
   d. ketosis.

10. What is the desirable BMI range for females?

   a. 18 to 20
   b. 19 to 21
   c. 21 to 23
   d. 23 to 25

11. Tim's desire to look good interferes with his relationship with others. Rather than spending his leisure time with family and friends, he spends a disproportionate amount of time exercising excessively at the gym and worrying about how his body looks. Tim suffers from

   a. social physique anxiety.
   b. appearance anxiety.
   c. obesity anxiety.
   d. anorexia nervosa.

12. Research on Pima Indians support:

   a. the Ob gene.
   b. body mass index.
   c. setpoint theory.
   d. adaptive thermogenesis.

13. A method of determining body fat in which a person assesses the amount of fat held between the thumb and index finger at various locations on the body is known as the:

   a. pinch test.
   b. skinfold caliper test.
   c. hydrostatic weighing technique.
   d. girth and circumference measure.

14. Eileen, who is very thin, is able to eat large amounts of food without gaining weight because the appetite center of her brain speeds up her metabolic activity to compensate for her increased consumption. This illustrates the concept of:

    a. hyperplasia.

    b. hypertrophy.

    c. satiety.

    d. adaptive thermogenesis.

15. What chemical signals the brain when you are full and need to stop eating?

    a. leptin

    b. keratin

    c. casein

    d. albumin

Practice Test 2

1. What is the ideal total body fat for men?

    a. 5–10 percent

    b. 11–15 percent

    c. 16–20 percent

    d. 25–35 percent

2. The method of determining body fat by measuring the amount of water displaced when a person is completely submerged is called the:

    a. skin-fold caliper test.

    b. body mass index.

    c. hydrostatic weighing technique.

    d. bioelectrical impedance analysis.

3. What technique of weight assessment is based on the relationship of weight to height?

    a. body composition index

    b. body mass index

    c. hydrostatic weight

    d. waist-to-hip ratio

4. Ellen is 50 percent above her ideal weight. She would be considered:

    a. mildly obese.

    b. moderately obese.

    c. severely obese.

    d. grossly obese.

5. Melissa frequently eats an abnormal amount of food in less than an hour, including a gallon of ice cream, a loaf of bread, a box of cookies, three candy bars, and a bag of popcorn. During this eating episode, she feels out of control and afterwards, feels guilty. What eating disorder does Melissa suffer from?

    a. pica

    b. anorexia nervosa

    c. bulimia nervosa

    d. binge eating disorder

6. Approximately 90 percent of the daily calorie expenditures of most people occur as a result of the:

    a. basal metabolic rate.

    b. resting metabolic rate

    c. exercise metabolic rate.

    d. sedentary metabolic rate.

7. What theory states that a person's body has a set amount of weight at which it is programmed to be comfortable?

    a. endocrine theory

    b. plateau theory

    c. setpoint theory

    d. adaptive thermogenesis theory

8. What percent of adolescents and young female adults are bulimic?

    a. 1 percent

    b. 3 percent

    c. 10 percent

    d. 33 percent

9. Which of the following is *not* a criterion for anorexia nervosa?

    a. refusal to maintain the minimum body weight for one's height and age

    b. intense fear of gaining weight even though underweight

    c. recurrent episodes of consuming a much larger amount of food than most people would during a similar time period

    d. disturbed perception of one's body weight or size

10. The energy expenditure of the body under BMR conditions plus other daily sedentary activities defines

    a. RMR.

    b. EMR.

    c. BMR.

    d. CMR.

11. What percent of the obese population have a thyroid problem?

    a. 2 percent

    b. 33 percent

    c. 50 percent

    d. 80 to 90 percent

12. For most people, the exercise metabolic rate accounts for what percent of all daily calorie expenditures?

    a. 10 percent

    b. 30 percent

    c. 70 percent

    d. 90 percent

13. One pound of body fat contains:

    a. 1,500 calories.

    b. 3,500 calories.

    c. 5,000 calories.

    d. 7,000 calories.

14. Jenny binge eats and then secretly vomits. What eating disorder does she suffer from?

    a. pica

    b. anorexia nervosa

    c. bulimia nervosa

    d. binge eating disorder

15. What percent of girls in late adolescence meet the full criteria for anorexia nervosa?

    a. 1 percent

    b. 5 percent

    c. 10 percent

    d. 33 percent

11

Personal Fitness

Chapter Overview

The benefits of regular physical activity include improved cardiorespiratory function, stronger muscles and bones, a decrease in stress and weight, increased immunity to disease, improved mental health, and prolonged life span. Unfortunately, most adults and many children do not get enough exercise. Heart disease and adult onset diabetes are increasing due to the increase in sedentary lifestyle.

Physical activity is any force exerted resulting in energy usage above the level used when the body is at rest. Increased physical activity decreases coronary heart disease, diabetes, osteoporosis, high blood pressure, cancers of the colon and reproductive organs, and psychosocial disorders such as depression and anxiety.

Physical fitness is the ability to exercise at a moderate to vigorous level on a regular basis without excessive fatigue. Exercise programs are designed to increase frequency, intensity, and duration of exercise to achieve a desired fitness level. Any individual, at any age, can achieve fitness without being an athlete. The key to becoming physically fit is to find an activity that is enjoyable and can be consistently done.

An aerobic exercise program for improving cardiorespiratory fitness should follow guidelines for frequency, intensity, and duration. Aerobic means "with oxygen" and describes exercise that increases the heart rate using the large muscles of the body and is performed at moderate intensity for extended periods of time. Aerobic capacity can be determined by a "treadmill test" administered by a professional and is more likely to be used with medical conditions such as asthma, diabetes, heart disease, or obesity.

Beginning exercisers should exercise at least three times per week as tolerated until 20–30 minutes each day five days per week is achieved. While exercising, heart rate should be monitored. Beginners should increase heart rate slightly and as physical conditioning improves, the target heart rate range can be increased. It is a good idea to monitor heart rate during aerobic activity or to use the "talk test" (if you can talk with a partner while exercising) as a guide. Persons who wish to lose weight should exercise with lower intensity so that they can exercise longer. The longer one exercises, the more calories are expended. The most successful weight loss programs

195

combine diet and exercise to reduce fatty tissue. Flexibility can be improved with stretching exercises and muscle strength and endurance can be improved with weight lifting or resistance training.

Injury prevention is an important part of any exercise program. Beginners may do too much too soon. Those who exercise sporadically may over-exercise. All exercisers should set challenging, but realistic exercise goals. Injuries are often associated with repetitive activities such as swimming, running, bicycling, and step aerobics. Overuse injuries of the leg, knee, shoulder, and elbow joints are common. Other injuries can occur through accidents or body contact. The best method for treating most exercise injuries is rest, ice, compression, and elevation. Any pain that lasts more than 30 minutes requires medical attention.

Proper equipment is essential to injury prevention. The appropriate type, size, fit, and care of athletic shoes is very important. Common injuries such as shin splints, plantar fasciitis, and "runner's knee" can be lessened with proper equipment and moderate training. Heat cramps, heat exhaustion, and heat stroke are common on hot and humid days. Drinking water or sports drinks frequently and resting in the shade can help. In cold weather, wearing several layers of clothing that do not retain moisture is important.

When designing your own fitness program, set realistic fitness goals, begin with warm-up exercise, then stretching and strength exercises before moving toward aerobic activity, and end with a cool-down period. The majority of the time should be spent on aerobic activity. The type of exercise is not as important as your enjoyment of the exercise. It should be something you like so you can have fun, look forward to it, and want to do it every day.

NAME: _____ DATE: _____

TAKE CHARGE WORKSHEET 11.1

At-Home Fitness Test

Some people rely on fitness professionals to administer a fitness test. One reason for this is that there are several methods for assessing various types of fitness. Some methods are strenuous or could cause injury to someone with cardiorespiratory, musculoskeletal, or metabolic limitations. When this is done, your measures would be compared with a "norm" table and an exercise program would be advised based on the results. Rather than comparing yourself with others, a better type of fitness test would be one that is relatively "harm free," that you could do yourself in the privacy of your own home, and use as a baseline or starting point so you can measure your own improvement over time. After four to eight weeks of regular exercise, you should see some changes.

Measuring Cardiorespiratory Fitness

DIRECTIONS: Before you get out of bed in the morning, take your pulse for one minute. Do this for three days and record the results below.

Day 1: _____ bpm   Day 2: _____ bpm   Day 3: _____ bpm

bpm = beats per minute

"Average" range is 70–72 bpm. "Fit" range is lower. "Unfit" range is higher

Measuring Lower Back and Hamstring Flexibility

DIRECTIONS: Before measuring your lower back and hamstring flexibility, your body needs to be warmed up. Perform some type of low intensity exercise until you begin to sweat (that is how you know you are fully warmed up). Then take off your shoes and sit on the floor with knees straight out in front of you. Without bending your knees, see how far past your toes you can touch. Try this three times and record your best stretch below.

_____ inches past the toes _____ touching the toes _____ inches from touching my toes

Measuring Lower Back and Abdominal Strength

DIRECTIONS: *Do not do this if you have shoulder, elbow, or wrist problems.* Lie on your back on the floor with your toes under the coffee table or sofa. Put your knees up at a 45 degree angle. Begin with your hands lying at your side. As you raise your torso up, touch your knees with your hand each time. Do not count the sit-up unless you touch your knees. See how many sit-ups you can do this way in one minute. Write the number here: _____ sit-ups in 1 minute

Measuring Shoulder and Upper Arm Fitness

DIRECTIONS: *Do not do this if you have shoulder, elbow, or wrist problems.* Place an item on the floor that is about the size of your fist and will not move. Position your chest over it. Men should do a full-body push-up. Females should do a modified (knees) push-up. Do not count the push-up unless your chest touches the object. See how many push-ups you can do this way in one minute. Write the number here: _____ push-ups in 1 minute

For Further Thought

Perform this fitness test again after you have been exercising 8 weeks. If some areas are not improving, then you may need to add upper body strengthening and flexibility exercises to your workout.

NAME: _____ DATE: _____

Progressive Exercise Program

If you would like to exercise for health reasons (lose weight or be less "winded"), then the following exercise program is designed for the beginning exerciser.

Initiating an Exercise Program

DIRECTIONS: Select a somewhat controlled environment for exercising, such as a running track. Allow approximately 30–45 minutes per workout. Begin with a warm up, then do aerobics, and cool down as follows:

Warm-up: Begin by doing light exercise until you begin to sweat.

Aerobics: Begin walking or running using the table below as a guideline.

Cool-down: After you stop walking or running, keep moving until your heart rate returns to normal and you are breathing normally. Stretch afterward.

Progressive Exercise Program

DIRECTIONS: A progressive exercise program increases first by time, then by intensity, then by frequency. Begin the progressive exercise program as recommended by the American College of Sports Medicine below.

> Week 1: Walk, jog, or bike 3 times per week for 12 minutes using the talk test*.
>
> Week 2: Walk, jog, or bike 3 times per week for 14 minutes increasing intensity slightly.
>
> Week 3: Walk, jog, or bike 3 times per week for 16 minutes increasing intensity slightly.
>
> Week 4: Walk, jog, or bike 3 times per week for 18 minutes increasing intensity slightly.
>
> Week 5: Walk, jog, or bike 3 times per week for 20 minutes increasing intensity slightly.
>
> Weeks 6–8: Walk, jog, or bike 3–4 times per week for 21 minutes increasing intensity slightly.
>
> Weeks 9–10: Walk, jog, or bike 3–4 times for 22 minutes at the same intensity.
>
> Weeks 11–13: Walk, jog, or bike 3–4 times for 24 minutes at the same intensity.
>
> Weeks 14–16: Walk, jog, or bike 3–4 times for 28 minutes at the same intensity.
>
> Weeks 17–19: Walk, jog, or bike 4–5 times for 28 minutes at the same intensity.
>
> Weeks 20–23: Walk, jog, or bike 4–5 times for 30 minutes at the same intensity.
>
> Weeks 24–27: Walk, jog, or bike 4–5 times for 30 minutes at the same intensity.
>
> Maintain weight or health status achieved: Walk, jog, or bike 3 times per week at the same or slightly higher intensity for 30–45 minutes to maintain weight loss or fitness level.

*The talk test means you can talk while you are doing it. If you cannot talk, then you need to decrease the intensity by slowing down your pace until you can talk.

Recording Your Progress

DIRECTIONS: Record your exercise behavior on the Aerobic Exercise Log in Take Charge Worksheet 11.3.

Recording Weight Loss

DIRECTIONS: Weigh yourself the same day and time of day one time per week with your shoes off. Record your weight below:

Weight at Week 1: _____ lbs.   Weight at Week 5: _____ lbs.

Weight at Week 2: _____ lbs.   Weight at Week 6: _____ lbs.

Weight at Week 3: _____ lbs.   Weight at Week 7: _____ lbs.

Weight at Week 4: _____ lbs.   Weight at Week 8: _____ lbs.

Recording Cardiorespiratory Improvement

DIRECTIONS: Record your heart rate before you begin your exercise program. Write your initial heart rate here: _____. Retake your resting heart rate after 8 weeks of consistent exercise. Write your new resting heart rate here: _____.

If your resting heart rate is the same, keep exercising and measure again later.

NAME: _____ DATE: _____

TAKE CHARGE WORKSHEET 11.3

Aerobic Exercise Log

DIRECTIONS: From the day you begin to exercise, use this log to record your activity. Plan to exercise each day. You may find that some days are easier to exercise than others. If you miss a workout, just record the reason and plan to exercise the next day. An example entry is provided.

Date and Time	Type of Activity	Number of Minutes	Feelings Before	Feelings After
Mon. 7:30AM	Walking	20 minutes	Tired	Energized

For Further Thought

If you begin to enjoy the activities you have already done, it may be time to try some other form of aerobic exercise. Try in-line or roller skating, an elliptical exerciser, basketball, soccer, or other continuous activity.

NAME: _____ DATE: _____

TAKE CHARGE WORKSHEET 11.4

Weight Training and Stretching Log

DIRECTIONS: For each week, record the number of repetitions (Rep) and weights (Wt) performed for each activity listed in the left column. Stretching exercises are included. Extra space is provided for additional activities you enjoy.

Activity **Weights or Resistance Machines**	Rep/Wt Week 1	Rep/Wt. Week 2	Rep/Wt. Week 3	Rep/Wt. Week 4	Rep/Wt. Week 5	Rep/Wt. Week 6
Bicep curl						
Tricep kick-back						
Flyes or Rowing						
Bench or Overhead Press						
Lat Pull-down						
Negative sit-ups						
Lunges						
Hip sled						
Leg extensions						
Leg curls						
Toe raises						
Calisthenics						
Sit-ups						
Push-ups						

Activity	Rep/Wt Week 1	Rep/Wt. Week 2	Rep/Wt. Week 3	Rep/Wt. Week 4	Rep/Wt. Week 5	Rep/Wt. Week 6
Stretches						
Neck from side to side						
Shoulder stretch						
Tricep stretch						
Rib/waist side to side						
Squat						
Groin stretch						
One leg extended stretch						
Ankle rotations						
Full body stretch						

Modify your workout when you design your new logsheet for subsequent weeks.

NAME: _____ DATE: _____

TAKE CHARGE WORKSHEET 11.5

How Much Do I Move?

DIRECTIONS: We often have an unrealistic perception of how much we actively move. Be as honest as possible when assessing the amount that you move during the average day. If it is different on weekends, fill out for days during the week and weekend separately.

1. Check mark those types of movement in which you participate.

_____ Walking	_____ Step Climbing	_____ Dancing
_____ Climbing	_____ Jumping rope	_____ Bicycling
_____ Lifting weights	_____ Physical labor	_____ Aerobics
_____ Tennis	_____ Hiking	_____ Yoga
_____ Lovemaking	_____ Jogging/Running	_____ Skiing
_____ Swimming	_____ Team sports	_____ Ice skating

2. Record the number of minutes or hours you spent moving or exercising for each of the time periods below

   Daily _____   Weekend _____

   Weekly _____   Monthly _____

3. Record the amount of time spent exercising during the month.

4. Do you spend as much time moving as you would like?

5. If not, in what types of activity would you like to participate?

6. What small change will you make toward improving your degree of movement?

7. What are you going to do today to implement the small change?

8. What will you do tomorrow?

9. What will you do this weekend?

10. What will you do this month?

11. What reward will you give yourself for meeting your objective?

NAME: _____ DATE: _____

TAKE CHARGE WORKSHEET 11.6

Test Your Exercise I.Q.

DIRECTIONS: Place a *T* in the space provided for a true statements and an *F* for a false statement.

_____ 1. The length of necessary cardiovascular exercise time on a stepping machine is less than the necessary cardiovascular exercise time on treadmills or bicycles.

_____ 2. People who exercise burn calories, even at rest.

_____ 3. Weight lifting builds muscles by producing miniscule rips and tears in muscle tissue.

_____ 4. Sports drinks are not as good as drinking cool water before, during, or after a workout.

_____ 5. The best time to stretch is before a workout.

_____ 6. If you stop abruptly rather than cooling down after intense exercise, complications can occur.

_____ 7. You must take your pulse while walking, jogging, or running to make sure you are not overdoing yourself.

_____ 8. It is normal to get shin splints when you begin a running program.

_____ 9. If all I want is "six pack abs" or to reduce abdominal fat, crunches are all I need.

_____ 10. Protein bars help you gain muscle mass quicker.

Answers

1. FALSE. In order to improve cardiovascular efficiency or lost weight, duration is more important than intensity. Stepping machines with resistance can cause dangerous increases in blood pressure for those who are at risk. Stepping machines are also especially hard on the knees. If you are in poor physical condition, walking or biking would be better.

2. TRUE. Exercising burns calories and the effects can continue for up to two hours after a workout, provided the workout is at least 15–20 minutes long and within the target heart rate range. This is true of aerobic and resistance exercise.

3. TRUE. In order to increase muscle size, some damage must occur, but it should be minimized by resting in between exercise bouts for approximately one day. You can do your upper body workout one day and the lower body workout the next day. It is normal for muscles to be sore up to 48 hours after lifting, but the soreness should diminish on its own. If the pain continues longer, your workout is too intense. You should lift less weight, reduce repetitions, or reduce the number of sets.

4. FALSE. Glucose in the body needs to be replenished after an intense workout lasting an hour or more, so sports drinks may actually be better in that regard. Many people do not drink as much water as they should. Sports drinks contain salt, which increases the thirst response, and sugar/flavoring, which encourages more drinking by children and adults. Either sports drinks or water is better than soft drinks or alcoholic beverages, which are dehydrating.

5. FALSE. Before stretching, the body needs to warm up. This can be done by performing light exercise until you begin to perspire. After you break a sweat, you can stretch with less discomfort. You can warm up, stretch, and then workout, or you can workout and then stretch. Experts are divided on whether stretching before or after exercising is better.

6. TRUE. If you have pre-existing medical problems or are at risk for cardiovascular or other diseases, stopping abruptly can initiate cardiac arrhythmias, a diabetic reaction, an asthmatic attack, nausea, or fainting. It is best to perform light exercise or walk around until the heart rate returns to normal before stopping.

7. FALSE. These methods are advised, but they may be inaccurate. You can wear a heart rate monitor or you can simply use the "talk test." (If you can talk to an exercise buddy or to yourself while exercising without becoming out of breath, you are probably within the target heart rate range.) Make sure, however, that you are challenging yourself.

8. FALSE. Some individuals will get shin splints, but it is usually caused by something that, if continued, will aggravate the problem. Shin splints can be caused by running on the balls (rather than the heels) of the feet, running uphill, having shoes without proper support, or having feet that simply are not made for running. If you get shin splints, you can put ice on the shins for 15 minutes, take it off for 15 minutes, and then reapply the ice until they feel better. You will want to stop running for a while until the inflammation decreases. Have your doctor, coach, or personal trainer examine your feet for pronation (flat feet), supination (high arches), or a combination of the two. Make sure that your shoes support the areas of your feet which may cause some of the problems. If the problem continues after modification, you may want to run in deep water, swim, bicycle, or walk.

9. FALSE. Fat around the abdominal area accumulates because of a fatty diet and insufficient aerobic activity. Crunches are anaerobic exercises which are not as effective for losing weight as walking, jogging, running, swimming, bicycling, and other aerobic activities. If you are still determined to perform abdominal crunches to tone the abdominal muscles, then be sure to include negative and diagonal sit-ups to include auxillary muscles.

10. FALSE. Protein bars may or may not be higher in protein content than regular granola, snack, or candy bars, even though they contain approximately the same number of calories per ounce.

General Review Questions

1. What are the benefits of regular physical activity?

2. What are the major components of physical fitness?

3. Why is osteoporosis more common among women than among men?

4. Describe the most common overuse injuries.

5. Identify and describe the different heat stress illnesses.

Practice Test 1

1. What effect does regular exercise have on lipoproteins?
   a. reduces the levels of LDLs and HDLs
   b. increases the levels of LDLs and HDLs
   c. reduces the levels of LDLs and increases the levels of HDLs
   d. increases the levels of LDLs and reduces the levels of HDLs

2. A test of aerobic capacity administered by a physician, exercise physiologist, or other trained person is called a(n):
   a. graded exercise test.
   b. maximum aerobic capacity test.
   c. aerobic endurance test.
   d. cardiac output test.

3. Osteoporosis is a disease characterized by:
   a. excessive thirst.
   b. low bone mass.
   c. digestive problems.
   d. high blood pressure.

4. The maximum volume of oxygen consumed by the muscles during exercise defines:

   a. aerobic capacity.

   b. target heart rate.

   c. maximum heart rate.

   d. conversational level of exercise.

5. What is the primary category of physical activity known to improve cardiovascular fitness?

   a. aerobic exercise

   b. anaerobic exercise

   c. flexibility

   d. body building

6. Which of the following statements about body composition and gender differences is true?

   a. Women have both a higher percentage of body fat and fat-free mass.

   b. Men have both a higher percentage of body fat and fat-free mass.

   c. Women have a higher percentage of body fat and a lower percentage of fat-free mass.

   d. Men have a higher percentage of body fat and a lower percentage of fat-free mass.

7. What component of physical fitness refers to the range of motion at a joint or a series of joints?

   a. flexibility

   b. body composition

   c. cardiorespiratory fitness

   d. muscular strength and endurance

8. Theresa wants to lower her ratio of fat weight to her total body weight. Theresa wants to work on her:

   a. flexibility.

   b. muscular endurance.

   c. muscular strength.

   d. body composition.

9. Yoga, tai chi, and pilates are three major styles of exercise that focus on

   a. flexibility.

   b. stretching.

   c. endurance.

   d. muscular strength.

10. What term is used for any pain that occurs below the knee and above the ankle?

    a. achilles tendonitis

    b. plantar fasciitis

    c. shin splints

    d. runner's knee

11. An effective resistance exercise program involves all of the following three key principles, *except* the

    a. tension principles.

    b. overload principle.

    c. specificity of training principle.

    d. flexibility principle.

12. Calisthenics refers to what resistance exercise method?

    a. fixed

    b. variable

    c. body weight

    d. accommodating

13. Jack went skiing and got lost for hours in frigid weather. His body core temperature dropped down to 93°F and he began to shiver and experienced amnesia before he was rescued. Jack suffered from:

    a. hyperthermia.

    b. hypothermia.

    c. hyperglycemia.

    d. hypoglycemia.

14. When Grace was playing on the monkey bars, she fell and broke her arm. What type of injury did she receive?

    a. underuse injury

    b. overuse injury

    c. traumatic injury

    d. intensity injury

15. After running in a marathon, Al experienced nausea, headache, fatigue, dizziness, and goosebumps. Al most likely has:

    a. heat cramps.

    b. heat exhaustion.

    c. heat stroke.

    d. hypothermia.

Practice Test 2

1. Janice has been lifting 95 pounds while doing three sets of 10 leg curls. To become stronger, she began lifting 105 pounds while doing leg curls. What principle of strength development does this represent?

    a. tension principle

    b. overload principle

    c. flexibility principle

    d. specificity of training principle

2. What is a 26-year-old male's maximum heart rate?

    a. 26

    b. 200

    c. 220

    d. 226

3. What type of muscle action is defined as force produced while the muscle is strengthening?

    a. isometric

    b. concentric

    c. eccentric

    d. hypocentric

4. Injuries that result from the cumulative effects of day-after-day stress placed on tendons, muscles, and joints are called:

    a. overuse injuries.

    b. traumatic injuries.

    c. overtraining injuries.

    d. repetitive injuries.

5. Joel enjoys various types of fitness exercises. He alternates his training days with jogging, cycling, and step aerobics. This type of training is called:

    a. cardiac fitness training.

    b. static training.

    c. cross training.

    d. multisport training.

6. The ability to sustain moderate-intensity whole-body activity for extended time periods defines

    a. flexibility.

    b. body composition.

    c. muscular strength and endurance.

    d. cardiorespiratory fitness.

7. What is RICE?

   a. components of setpoint theory

   b. components of first-aid treatment

   c. components of exercise

   d. components of cross training

8. Megan regularly swims and jogs as her exercise program. Her alternating of these two exercises illustrates:

   a. RICE.

   b. overuse injury.

   c. cross training.

   d. frequency, intensity, and duration.

9. To measure Bill's maximal aerobic capacity, an exercise physiologist had him exercise on a treadmill. Bill initially walked at an easy pace, and then, at set intervals, gradually increased the workload to the point of maximal exertion. What was this called?

   a. graded exercise test

   b. metabolic rate test

   c. blood pressure test

   d. duration test

10. What is known as the "conversational level of exercise"?

   a. target heart rate of 30 percent of maximum

   b. target heart rate of 50 percent of maximum

   c. target heart rate of 70 percent of maximum

   d. target heart rate of 90 percent of maximum

11. What is the most frequent cause of shin splints?

   a. aerobics

   b. running

   c. bicycling

   d. swimming

12. Which of the following is the most severe form of heat stress illnesses?

   a. heat cramps

   b. heat stroke

   c. heat exhaustion

   d. hypothermia

13. What condition occurs as a result of body heat being lost faster than it is produced?

   a. hypothermia

   b. heat stroke

   c. heat cramps

   d. heat exhaustion

14. What component of physical fitness is defined as the ability to sustain moderate-intensity whole-body activity for extended time periods?

   a. flexibility

   b. body composition

   c. cardiorespiratory fitness

   d. muscular strength and endurance

15. An ancient Chinese form of exercise widely practiced in the West today that promotes balance, coordination, stretching, and meditation is called

   a. yoga.

   b. qi gong.

   c. tai chi.

   d. pilates.

12

Cardiovascular Disease

Chapter Overview

Cardiovascular disease is the leading cause of death around the world. Most of these deaths are the result of cardiac arrests, meaning the heart stops, and even with cardiopulmonary resuscitation (CPR), they are not preventable. A heart attack occurs when blood circulation to the heart muscle is blocked. The heart acts as a pump, moving blood, which contains nutrients, oxygen, waste products, hormones and enzymes, through the body. The blood passes through four chambers that are separated by valves, which prevent blood from flowing backward. The average heartbeat is 70–80 beats per minute. There are many heart diseases that cause the heart to function improperly. Among these diseases are arrhythmia or irregular heartbeat, congenital heart disease, which is found at birth, and rheumatic heart disease, which may result from an untreated case of strep throat in early childhood.

Blood flows away from the heart through arteries, and travels back to the heart through veins. Fat and cholesterol can build up in the arteries, making it difficult for the blood to pass. There are two kinds of fat in the blood, known as cholesterol and triglycerides. When the heart is getting less oxygen than it needs, severe chest pain or angina pectoris may occur. When the heart muscle is weakened, blood backs up in the veins, causing fluid accumulation in legs or lungs. This accumulation of blood away from the heart can result in congestive heart failure. A stroke occurs when circulation to the brain is disrupted due to a blood clot or an aneurysm.

Controllable risk factors include quitting smoking, reducing stress, controlling ideal body weight range, reducing saturated fats and cholesterol in the diet, reducing high blood pressure, reducing sodium in the diet, and exercising. The most important of these are to stop smoking and to lose weight. A healthy heart may be maintained through a diet low in fat and cholesterol and an increase in soluble fiber from fruits, vegetables, legumes, seeds, and bran. Controlling diet and stress while increasing exercise can also lower blood pressure.

Hereditary predisposition, age, gender, and race are all factors that cannot be controlled. The number of women having heart attacks is increasing. Hormone replacement therapy after menopause decreases risk but more research needs to be done regarding hormones and cardiac health. Prevention of cardiovascular disease can save billions in dollars that accrue from premature death, disability, and medical expenses.

The following techniques are used to diagnose cardiovascular disease: electrocardiogram (ECG), angiogram, positron emission scan (PET), radionuclide imaging, magnetic resonance imaging, and digital cardiac angiography. Angioplasty and coronary bypass surgery are often necessary to prevent a heart attack or the recurrence of a heart attack. Cardiac rehabilitation includes exercise training, health education classes on good nutrition, and CVD risk management.

TAKE CHARGE WORKSHEET 12.1

Cardiovascular Risk Assessment

DIRECTIONS: Check the risk factors that apply to you.

Risk Factors

Uncontrollable risk factors

_____ Male

_____ Parent suffered a heart attack or stroke before age 60

_____ Parent with diabetes

_____ Parent with high blood pressure

_____ Parent with high cholesterol

Controllable risk factors

_____ Smoker

_____ Live or work with a smoker

_____ Blood pressure above 130/80

_____ Cholesterol higher than 200

_____ Exercise less than 1–2 times per week

_____ 10 pounds above ideal weight

_____ Frequently feel stressed

_____ Frequently irritated or angry

Options for a Healthy Heart

DIRECTIONS: Develop a plan for regulating the controllable factors you checked. Select options below that you could do to reduce your risk of cardiovascular disease.

_____ Stop smoking.

_____ Stop going out to bars where people smoke.

_____ Ask the person who smokes not to do it when you are around.

_____ Find a job in a non-smoking environment.

_____ Reduce consumption of fatty foods.

_____ Reduce alcohol consumption.

_____ Drink more water.

_____ Exercise inside more often.

_____ Exercise outside more often.

_____ Join a health club or an intramural team.

_____ Lose weight.

_____ Eat more fruits, vegetables, legumes (beans), and whole grains.

_____ Take breaks when you get upset.

_____ Try not to get upset over little things.

_____ Limit your anger to things that truly matter.

_____ Visualize yourself living a healthier lifestyle.

Reducing Your Risk

DIRECTIONS: Using the options checked above, develop an action plan for how to reduce risk factors for cardiovascular disease. Tell a friend about it, and ask them to help you make the lifestyle changes that you need for a healthy heart.

NAME: _____ DATE: _____

TAKE CHARGE WORKSHEET 12.2

Monitoring Blood Pressure and Cholesterol

Monitoring Blood Pressure

The first sound heard as a blood pressure cuff is deflated is the systolic measure. The last sound heard is the diastolic measure. Systolic pressure tells you how hard your heart needs to pump blood through the arteries when it is at work. Diastolic pressure tells you how hard your heart needs to pump when it is at rest.

DIRECTIONS: Have your blood pressure taken by a professional. Do not use the machines at the pharmacy or department store because the equipment needs to be calibrated frequently to have an accurate measure. Do not compare the results from one test to another unless the same person with the same equipment uses the same procedure to measure your blood pressure.

My blood pressure was: _____ mm Hg.

Blood pressure varies with age. A young person should have a blood pressure of about 120/80 or less. An older person may have a higher blood pressure reading. What is more important is the difference between the systolic and the diastolic measures. If the blood pressure is 140/100, the person is usually referred to a physician for monitoring.

Monitoring Cholesterol

There are two types of cholesterol: high-density lipoprotein (HDL) and low-density lipoprotein (LDL). LDL cholesterol builds up on artery walls. HDL cholesterol seems to clean out the LDL cholesterol in the blood. Restricting saturated fat in the diet in favor of monounsaturated and polyunsaturated fat will lower LDL cholesterol. Exercise can increase HDL cholesterol. The ratio of LDL/HDL cholesterol is more important than the total measure of cholesterol.

The best measure for cholesterol is a fasting cholesterol test. You should not eat or drink anything for 12 hours prior to the test. Test results will be available a few days after blood is drawn from the arm. This type of test will give you total cholesterol, LDL, HDL, and cholesterol ratios. A frequently used method for health fairs is the finger-stick method. A small amount of blood is drawn from the finger into a pipette and then analyzed by a machine. It will only give you a total cholesterol reading and may not be a true test because there was no fasting involved.

DIRECTIONS: If you have never had your cholesterol checked, ask the student health center or your family practitioner to check your cholesterol. Write the results of your cholesterol test here.

My cholesterol level was: _____ dl/mg. Recommended cholesterol levels are below 200 dl/mg. Plan to have blood pressure and cholesterol evaluated at least once every year.

NAME: _____ DATE: _____

TAKE CHARGE WORKSHEET 12.3

Cutting Out the Fat

Many of the foods we enjoy today have high levels of fat. Foods highest in fat are the ones we are most likely to eat when we are away from home. Below is a list of things you can do when eating out to reduce your fat intake.

DIRECTIONS: Check those statements that you are willing to do the next time you eat out. Bring this list with you the next time you dine out.

_____ Limit eating out to one time per week.

_____ Order water instead of an alcoholic drink.

_____ Order foods that are broiled, boiled, or grilled (not fried).

_____ Ask the waiter or waitress if they use butter or gravies on the main entrée and, if so, could they use less of it, before you order that dish.

_____ If warm, fresh bread is served, try eating it without butter or use a very small amount.

_____ Forego the appetizer, but if you want a low-fat one, try bruschetta (low fat).

_____ Order a baked potato instead of French fries.

_____ Have either sour cream or butter (but not both) on your baked potato.

_____ Order French dressing, vinaigrette, or oil and vinegar, rather than creamy dressings.

_____ Order dressing on the side so you can control how much goes on your salad.

_____ Avoid cheesecake, ice cream, or pie for dessert.

DIRECTIONS: Check the statements that you are willing to do at home. Bring this list when you go shopping and refer to it when preparing meals.

_____ Buy reduced-calorie butter/margarine and salad dressings.

_____ Buy skim milk instead of whole, 2%, or 1%.

_____ Try ice milk or yogurt instead of ice cream.

_____ Buy thin crust pizza instead of deep dish, pan, or tossed.

_____ Buy bagels and spread the cream cheese lightly.

_____ Toast English muffins or bread instead of toaster pastries.

_____ Instead of pancakes and sausage or bacon, try cooked cereals.

_____ Instead of hot dogs or lunch meats try turkey or chicken breast.

_____ Limit use of peanut butter.

_____ Use salsa instead of cheese sauce with tortilla chips.

_____ When making a cake or other recipe, reduce the fat by one-third.

_____ Keep fresh fruits and vegetables around for snacks.

_____ Limit yourself to one chocolate bar per week.

_____ Try mozzarella or hard cheeses and use them sparingly.

_____ After cooking a piece of chicken, remove the skin.

_____ Trim the fat from meats after you cook them.

_____ Buy hamburger that is 70–85% leaner.

_____ Avoid buying potato chips or other snacks in a bag.

_____ Try not to use cream sauces in casseroles or on foods.

_____ Try poached eggs rather than fried or scrambled.

NAME: _____ DATE: _____

TAKE CHARGE WORKSHEET 12.4

Healthy Heart I.Q.

DIRECTIONS: Circle either *T* for true or *F* for false. Answers are found on the back of this worksheet.

T   F   1. High blood pressure is a controllable risk factor for heart disease.

T   F   2. Omega-3 fatty acids, found in fish oils, are recommended to reduce serum cholesterol.

T   F   3. There are often no symptoms for high blood pressure.

T   F   4. High blood pressure is caused by stress.

T   F   5. Reducing sodium intake will reduce high blood pressure.

T   F   6. Drinking alcohol each day is good for your heart and blood vessels.

T   F   7. Of all the risk factors that you can change, smoking cessation has the most dramatic effect for reducing the risk of a stroke or a heart attack.

T   F   8. The safest and most effective way to lose weight and keep it off is to increase physical activity and eat fewer calories.

T   F   9. It is not necessary for children or young adults to have their cholesterol checked.

T   F   10. Crude fiber is the best type of fiber to eat to reduce cholesterol.

Answers

1. TRUE. High blood pressure is a warning sign that your cardiovascular system is not working properly. A high systolic and diastolic reading means that your heart is working harder at work and at rest then the heart of someone with a blood pressure within a normal range.

2. FALSE. Omega-3 fatty acids are a type of polyunsaturated fat. They are not known to lower cholesterol levels in the blood. Fish is usually lower in fat, however, than red meats.

3. TRUE. High blood pressure is often referred to as the "silent killer" because you can have high blood pressure and not know it. Some people do have ringing in their ears, dizziness, or headaches, but not everyone. It is a good idea to have your blood pressure checked on a regular basis, particularly if you have a hereditary predisposition for high blood pressure.

4. FALSE. Blood pressure can be elevated by stress, but only temporarily. The type of high blood pressure to be concerned about is the type that is persistent over time.

5. FALSE. It is true that Americans have more sodium in their diet than they need and that they are an overweight society. Whether you have high blood pressure or not, it is a good idea to monitor sodium intake to approximately one teaspoon per day. If your sodium intake is very high, blood pressure may be decreased, but other factors may persist so that blood pressure is only minimally affected.

6. FALSE. Drinking too much alcohol will actually increase blood pressure. Some individuals feel that one alcoholic beverage (12 ounces of beer, 4–5 ounces of wine, 1.0 ounce of 80 proof, 1.5 ounces of 100 proof distilled beverage) per day helps them to relax and it may be beneficial. Using cardiovascular fitness as a reason to drink, however, may be dangerous.

7. TRUE. You can watch your cholesterol and your blood pressure, but smoking affects both of these factors, as well as your respiratory efficiency. There is nothing more important that you can do for your health than to stop smoking.

8. TRUE. There are many ways to lose weight, but once you stop using those methods and continue your inactive lifestyle and eating habits, the weight will return or increase. The only way to lose weight and keep the weight off is to change your lifestyle.

9. FALSE. Children from families with a history of high cholesterol (200 mg/dL or above) and whose family members have had heart disease at an early age (55 years of age or younger) should have their cholesterol levels monitored. College students may unknowingly have high cholesterol.

10. FALSE. There are three different types of fiber: crude, insoluble, and soluble fiber. All types of fiber help to move food through the digestive tract faster, cutting down the time fats are metabolized before they are excreted. Crude fiber is found in seeds, nuts, and whole grains. Insoluble fiber is found in most grains. Soluble fiber is found in fruits and vegetables. Actually, it is the soluble fiber that does the most to reduce serum cholesterol.

General Review Questions

1. Identify different types of cardiovascular disease.

2. What are the risk factors for cardiovascular disease that we can control?

3. Describe the basic steps involved in heart function.

4. Describe the diagnostic techniques used to detect heart disease.

5. What are three main reasons for the widespread neglect of the signs of heart disease in women?

Practice Test 1

1. Vessels that carry blood away from the heart to other regions of the body are called the:
   a. atrium.
   b. veins.
   c. capillaries.
   d. arteries.

2. An irregularity in heartbeat is called a(n):
   a. fibrillation.
   b. bradycardia.
   c. tachycardia.
   d. arrhythmia.

3. What occurs when the blood supply to the brain is interrupted?
   a. stroke
   b. thrombosis
   c. myocardial infarction
   d. aneurysm

4. A surgical technique whereby a blood vessel is implanted to bypass a blocked artery is called:
   a. angioplasty.
   b. coronary bypass surgery.
   c. electrocardiogram.
   d. pacemaker implantation.

5. What is the term for an abnormally slow heartbeat?

   a. arrhythmia

   b. tachycardia

   c. bradycardia

   d. aneurysm

6. What is the leading single cause of death around the world?

   a. lung cancer

   b. homicide

   c. accidents

   d. cardiovascular disease

7. What type of blood vessels have thin walls that permit the exchange of oxygen, carbon dioxide, nutrients, and waste products with body cells?

   a. arteries

   b. arterioles

   c. capillaries

   d. veins

8. Severe chest pain occurring as a result of reduced oxygen flow to the heart is called:

   a. angina pectoris.

   b. arrhythmias.

   c. myocardial infarction.

   d. congestive heart failure.

9. The heart is a _____-chambered pump.

   a. two

   b. three

   c. four

   d. five

10. Richard complains of a "racing heart" even though he has not been exercising. He may be experiencing:

    a. fibrillation.

    b. arrhythmia.

    c. tachycardia.

    d. bradycardia.

11. Debbie has rheumatic heart disease caused by:

    a. excessive weight gain.

    b. excessive weight loss.

    c. an unresolved streptococcal infection.

    d. severe hypertension.

12. Transient ischemic attacks (TIAs) are often indicators of an impending:

    a. stroke.

    b. angina pectoris.

    c. coronary thrombosis.

    d. arrhythmia.

13. Which of the following is the most effective technique for measuring heart activity?

    a. angiography

    b. electrocardiogram

    c. positron emission tomography scan

    d. digital cardiac angiography

14. Even though Susan's blood pressure is normal when it is checked at the doctor's office, it increases dramatically when she is under everyday stress. Susan is a:

    a. hot reactor.

    b. cold reactor.

    c. hyperreactor.

    d. hyporeactor.

15. Bill experiences chest pain whenever he goes running. The chest pain occurs as a result of reduced oxygen flow to his heart. Bill's chest pain is called

a. angina pectoris.

b. arrhythmia.

c. fibrillation.

d. collateral circulation.

Practice Test 2

1. What is the term for an abnormally fast heartbeat?

a. arrhythmia

b. fibrillation

c. bradycardia

d. tachycardia

2. A thrombus, an embolus, and an aneurysm all may cause

a. a stroke.

b. congestive heart failure.

c. arrhythmia.

d. rheumatic heart disease.

3. What percent of all cases of hypertension are known as essential hypertension?

a. 10 percent

b. 50 percent

c. 68 percent

d. 90 percent

4. What blood pressure value refers to pressure being applied to the walls of the arteries when the heart contracts?

a. diastolic pressure

b. systolic pressure

c. normal pressure

d. contraction pressure

5. The diagnostic technique in which a needle-thin catheter is threaded through blocked arteries of the heart, a dye is injected, and an X-ray is taken to find the blocked areas is called:

a. angiography.

b. radionuclide imaging.

c. electocardiogram.

d. positron emission tomography.

6. Under normal circumstances, the body contains _____ quarts of blood.

a. 4

b. 6

c. 8

d. 10

7. What is the term for the thickening or hardening of the arteries?

a. myocardial infarction

b. cerebrovascular accident

c. atherosclerosis

d. arrhythmia

8. What two key components of the Type A personality increase young adults' risk of developing high blood pressure?

a. impatience and hostility

b. depression and gender

c. depression and anxiety

d. gender and hostility

9. A weakening in a blood vessel that causes it to bulge and, in severe cases, burst is called:

   a. congestive heart failure.

   b. angina pectoris.

   c. an aneurysm.

   d. an arrhythmia.

10. Bill's blood pressure is 150 over 94. What is this classification?

    a. normal

    b. mild hypertension

    c. moderate hypertension

    d. severe hypertension

11. What is the greatest killer?

    a. stroke

    b. angina pectoris

    c. atherosclerosis

    d. coronary heart disease

12. Nitroglycerin, calcium channel blockers, and beta blockers are used to treat:

    a. angina pectoris.

    b. coronary heart disease.

    c. atherosclerosis.

    d. strokes.

13. Which of the following methods involves injecting a person with a radioactive tracer that is scanned electronically to produce a three-dimensional image of the heart and arteries?

    a. angiography

    b. electrocardiogram

    c. magnetic resonance imaging

    d. positron emission tomography

14. An electrocardiogram (ECG) is a record of the electrical activity of the:

    a. brain.

    b. heart.

    c. facial muscles.

    d. body muscles.

15. What disease is the "silent killer" because it has no symptoms, 20 percent of people who have the condition don't know they have it, and only one-third of those who are aware of it have it under control?

    a. angina pectoris

    b. arrhythmia

    c. hypertension

    d. atherosclerosis

13
Cancer

Chapter Overview

Cancer consists of the uncontrolled growth and spread of abnormal cells. Abnormal cells can amass into tumors. All of us may have cancer cells in our body, but under normal conditions they do not cause harm. A change in the immune system or in the environment preferred by normal cells can cause new growth (neoplasm) or a tumor to occur. Some tumors are benign (noncancerous) and others are malignant (cancerous). Benign tumors are usually enclosed in a shell or capsule and do not spread to other body areas. Malignant tumors have the ability to spread. The best way to determine the type of tumor is to have a biopsy done. Benign tumors can be successfully treated, but metastasis (the spread of cancerous cells) is difficult to treat.

Anyone can develop cancer, but those with a family history of cancer are at a higher risk. Some risk factors can be controlled, such as smoking, fat consumption, weight, and exposure to environmental hazards such as asbestos, chemicals, pollution, radiation, and ultraviolet rays. Some believe that social and psychological factors play some role in determining who gets cancer and who does not. There seems to be evidence that some cancers are caused by viruses but other factors may contribute as well.

There are four categories of cancer: carcinomas, sarcomas, lymphomas, and leukemia. Carcinomas are found in the breast, lung, intestines, skin, and mouth. Sarcomas are found in bones, muscles, and connective tissue. Lymphomas invade the lymph system. Leukemias affect blood-forming bone marrow and the spleen.

Smoking causes lung cancer in both smokers and nonsmokers (via second-hand smoke). Young men and women, as well as older adults, can develop skin, breast, uterine, testicular, or colon cancer. Prostate or ovarian cancer usually develops in older males and females. Pancreatic cancer and leukemia are difficult to treat, but individuals do go into remission when the cancer growth subsides for a period of time. Some cancer survivors experience trouble getting jobs, health insurance, or life insurance because they are considered a high risk. Chemotherapy, radiation therapy, and surgery are the most common methods used to stop the growth and spread of cancer cells. Research is being conducted to find a cancer vaccine or anticancer drugs.

Detecting cancer early can save a life. Thankfully, through research efforts and better tests, the diagnosis of cancer does not always have to be a death sentence, though it should still be considered serious enough to warrant attention and to motivate preventive actions. Self-examinations and self-referrals to physicians for more sophisticated tests can save time and money or lend you peace of mind.

TAKE CHARGE WORKSHEET 13.1

Cancer Risk Assessment

DIRECTIONS: Check or fill out the information below if it pertains to you.

Family History

Father had _____ cancer.

Mother had _____ cancer.

Sister had _____ cancer.

Brother had _____ cancer.

Paternal grandfather had _____ cancer.

Paternal grandmother had _____ cancer.

Maternal grandfather had _____ cancer.

Maternal grandmother had _____ cancer.

Personal Health History

_____ I smoke or use smokeless tobacco.

_____ I am constantly exposed to tobacco smoke.

_____ I live in an area with heavy air pollution.

_____ I have fair skin.

_____ I have been sunburned several times.

_____ I like to lay in the sun or use tanning beds.

_____ I rarely use sunscreen.

_____ I am overweight.

_____ I am sedentary (watch more than one hour of television per week).

_____ I have a high-fat diet.

_____ I have a low-fiber diet.

_____ I do not eat many fruits.

_____ I do not eat many vegetables.

_____ I drink more than 1 (female) or 2 (male) alcoholic drinks per day.

_____ I have had genital warts or herpes (females only).

Personal Health Examination History

_____ I have never had a Pap smear (females only).

_____ I do not regularly check my breasts (females)/testicles (males) for lumps.

_____ I have never had a physical examination by a doctor.

_____ I have never had a mammogram (only for women over 40).

_____ It has been a long time since I have seen a dentist.

_____ I have some skin problems, but I have never seen a dermatologist.

_____ I have never had a rectal examination (males only).

Cancer Symptoms

_____ I have a mole or a patch of skin that never seems to heal.

_____ I have moles that are irregular in color and have irregular borders.

_____ I have found a lump in my breast or testicle.

_____ I am hoarse or have a sore throat most of the time.

_____ I have a cough that doesn't seem to go away.

_____ I have a white or tough area on my cheek or gums.

_____ I have seen blood in my urine or stool.

NAME: _____ DATE: _____

TAKE CHARGE WORKSHEET 13.2

Breast Self-Examination

Breast cancer can be found in women of any age. Women with higher body fat and high-fat diets are more likely to develop breast cancer, particularly if their mothers had breast cancer.

DIRECTIONS: Anytime you notice a discharge, dimple, or lump on your breast, perform a breast self-examination. Otherwise, each month, 1–2 days after your menstrual period ends, follow this procedure recommended by the American Cancer Society.

1. Sit or stand in front of a mirror with arms by your side. Turn from side to side to check breasts for:
   a. change in breast size or shape,
   b. puckering or dimpling of the skin, or
   c. change in size or position of one nipple compared to the other.

2. Raise your arms above your head and repeat these observations.

3. Gently press each nipple with your fingertips to see if there is any discharge.

4. Lie down and put a pillow or folded bath towel under your left shoulder. Place your left hand under your head.

5. Imagine that your breast is divided into quarters. With your right hand (fingers together), use small circular motions to feel the inner, upper quarter of your left breast. Start at your breastbone and work toward the nipple. Do the same with the lower, inner portion of your breast.

6. Move your left arm by your side and feel under your left armpit for swelling.

7. With your arm still down, feel the upper, outer part of your breast, starting with your nipple and working outwards. Examine the lower, outer quarter the same way.

8. Repeat this procedure on the right breast using the left hand.

9. Report any unusual changes to your gynecologist or family physician. They will want to repeat the procedure again. If any unusual thickening, lumps, swollen lymph glands, or discharge is noted, you may be referred for a mammogram.

The mammogram procedure consists of placing the breast between two metal plates while an X-ray is taken. If a lump is found, a biopsy will be performed to determine if the lump is benign or malignant.

NAME: _____ DATE: _____

Testicular Self-Examination

Testicular cancer can be found in young men, particularly athletes. Lance Armstrong and other young men have detected testicular cancer early and have sent a powerful message to encourage self-examination.

DIRECTIONS: Each month, on approximately the same day, follow this procedure recommended by the National Cancer Institute.

1. After a warm bath or shower, stand in front of a mirror and check for swelling on the scrotum (skin). The heat from the bath or shower makes abnormalities easier to find.

2. Examine each testicle with both hands. Place the index and middle fingers under the testicle with thumbs placed on top. Roll the testicle gently between the thumbs and fingers. Don't be alarmed if one testicle seems slightly larger than the other. That is normal.

3. Find the epididymis, the soft, tube-like structure behind the testicle that collects and carries sperm. If you become familiar with this structure, you will not mistake it for a suspicious lump. Cancerous lumps are usually found on the sides of the testicle, but can also be found on the front.

4. If you find a lump, see a doctor right away for a diagnosis. The abnormality may not be cancer, but if it is, it can spread if left untreated.

5. If you do not find a lump, check each month for any changes.

General Review Questions

1. What is cancer?

2. Discuss the various lifestyle risk factors for cancer.

3. What are the risk factors for breast cancer?

4. Explain how benign and malignant tumors differ.

5. Outline the ABCD rule for the warning signs of melanoma.

Practice Test 1

1. In the United States, what is the lifetime risk of developing cancer for men?

   a. one in two

   b. one in three

   c. one in four

   d. one in six

2. What is the most common carcinogen?

   a. asbestos

   b. tar in cigarettes

   c. smog

   d. pesticides

3. Suspected cancer-causing genes that are present on chromosomes are called:

   a. epigenes.

   b. oncogenes.

   c. primogenes.

   d. metastogenes.

4. Barbara is a physician who specializes in the treatment of malignancies. Barbara is a(n):

   a. internist.

   b. oncologist.

   c. endocrinologist.

   d. epidemiologist.

5. What is the greatest risk factor for cancer?

    a. obesity

    b. smoking

    c. hormones

    d. chronic infections

6. Cancers that arise from epithelial tissues, the most common sites for cancers, are called:

    a. leukemias.

    b. lymphomas.

    c. sarcomas.

    d. carcinomas.

7. Cancer of the blood-forming parts of the body, particularly the bone marrow and spleen, is called:

    a. lymphoma.

    b. leukemia.

    c. carcinoma.

    d. sarcoma.

8. What classification of cancer metastasizes primarily via the blood in the early stages of disease?

    a. leukemias

    b. lymphomas

    c. sarcomas

    d. carcinomas

9. Hodgkin's disease is a type of:

    a. sarcoma.

    b. carcinoma.

    c. lymphoma.

    d. leukemia.

10. Cancers that occur in the mesodermal layers of tissue are called:

    a. carcinomas.

    b. lymphomas.

    c. leukemia.

    d. sarcomas.

11. A large group of diseases characterized by uncontrolled growth and spread of abnormal cells is called:

    a. mutant cells.

    b. neoplasms.

    c. carcinogens.

    d. cancer.

12. The most dangerous carcinogen is:

    a. coal tar.

    b. tar in cigarettes.

    c. asbestos.

    d. pesticides.

13. What type of skin cancer treatment involves tissue destruction by freezing?

    a. electrodesiccation

    b. crysosurgery

    c. chemotherapy

    d. radiation therapy

14. What is the *lifetime risk* of developing breast cancer?

    a. 1 in 8

    b. 1 in 20

    c. 1 in 75

    d. 1 in 90

15. Risk factors for breast cancer include all of the following, *except*:

    a. female, under the age of 20.

    b. family history, in particular a grandmother, mother, or sister.

    c. female, never had children.

    d. female, first child after the age of 30.

Practice Test 2

1. Persons from what racial and ethnic group are most likely to develop cancer?

   a. Whites

   b. Hispanics

   c. Asian Americans

   d. African Americans

2. What is the lifetime risk for developing cancer in the United States?

   a. Men have a lifetime risk of one in two; women have a lifetime risk of one in three.

   b. Women have a lifetime risk of one in two; men have a lifetime risk of one in three.

   c. Men and women have a lifetime risk of one in four.

   d. Men and women have a lifetime risk of one in eight.

3. What is the leading cancer killer for both men and women?

   a. lung cancer

   b. breast cancer

   c. skin cancer

   d. colon cancer

4. Which of the following increases a woman's risk of breast cancer?

   a. low parity

   b. late menopause

   c. early menarche

   d. hormone replacement therapy

5. The American Cancer Society states that cigarette smoking is responsible for what percent of all cancer deaths?

   a. 10 percent

   b. 20 percent

   c. 30 percent

   d. 50 percent

6. Skin cancer is a type of:

   a. sarcoma.

   b. lymphoma.

   c. leukemia.

   d. carcinoma.

7. What are the most common sites for cancers?

   a. bone marrow

   b. lymphatic system

   c. epithelial tissues

   d. mesodermal tissues

8. Breast cancer is a:

   a. lymphoma.

   b. leukemia.

   c. sarcoma.

   d. carcinoma.

9. Most uterine cancers develop in the:

   a. cervix.

   b. vagina.

   c. fallopian tubes.

   d. endometrium.

10. What is the five-year survival rate for people with localized breast cancer?

    a. 23 percent

    b. 59 percent

    c. 72 percent

    d. 97 percent

11. Bleeding from the rectum, blood in the stool, and changes in bowel habits are the major warning signals of:

    a. prostate cancer.

    b. colorectal cancer.

    c. liver cancer.

    d. pancreatic cancer.

12. What is the most common cancer in the United States today?

    a. skin cancer

    b. breast cancer

    c. lung cancer

    d. prostate cancer

13. What is the most common sign of ovarian cancer?

    a. fatigue

    b. pain during intercourse

    c. enlargement of the abdomen

    d. unexplained weight loss

14. The process by which cancer spreads from one area to different areas in the body is called:

    a. metastasis.

    b. biopsy.

    c. virulence.

    d. mutation.

15. In general, ordinary-looking cells enclosed in a fibrous shell or capsule that prevents their spreading to other body areas are called:

    a. mutant cells.

    b. malignant tumors.

    c. benign tumors.

    d. metastatic tumors.

14

Infectious and Noninfectious Conditions

Chapter Overview

Disease-causing pathogens are found everywhere, come in many forms, and are transmitted in various ways. Disease transmission is classified as air-borne, food-borne, animal-borne, water-borne, or transmitted from mother to infant. Bacterial infections include staph, strep, pneumonia, Legionnaire's disease, tuberculosis, and gum diseases. Most bacterial infections can be treated with antibiotics. Viruses, which live in healthy cells, are difficult to treat because to kill a virus means to kill healthy cells in the body. Viruses cause the common cold, flu, mononucleosis, hepatitis, and measles. Other pathogens include fungi, protozoa, parasites, and prions.

The immune system consists of antigens, lymphocytes, white blood cells, lymph nodes, bone marrow, and other glands. B-cells and T-cells are lymphocytes that fight or kill pathogens and have a role in developing immunity to a disease. Our body uses other mechanisms such as fever and pain to help fight an infection. Vaccinations also help boost immunity and fight disease.

New diseases are emerging while some of the diseases we thought were controlled or eradicated are recurring in different places or in different forms. The increase in global travel has also contributed to the increased spread of disease. Bioterrorism is the newest threat of disease transmission.

Sexually transmitted diseases (STDs) or infections (STIs) are not new, but they are still a major concern, particularly among college students. STIs are easily spread because of high sexual activity, lack of preventive measures, and the possibility that an individual can be infected and be unaware of it. The more sexual partners one has, the more likely they are to acquire an STI. STIs are spread through mucous membranes and from oral, genital, or anal contact. Several STIs are difficult to detect, such as chlamydia, PID, gonorrhea, and syphilis. These STIs are likely to be spread before they are treated. Lice, warts, yeast infections, protozoan infections, UTIs, and herpes are common as well.

Probably the scariest virus outbreak in this decade has been the spread of the human immunodeficiency virus (HIV), which leads to acquired immune deficiency syndrome (AIDS). Infection with HIV occurs from contact with body fluids such as vaginal secretions, sperm, and blood. Symptoms of HIV may take months or years to appear. It may take 8–10 years before AIDS develops. The ELISA test can detect antibody production, which is usually an indicator of exposure to HIV. Some drugs have been developed to treat AIDS in order to prolong life, but there is still no cure.

Chronic diseases can affect the respiratory, neurological, digestive, and musculoskeletal systems. Chronic respiratory problems include allergies, hay fever, asthma, bronchitis, and emphysema. Neurological disorders include migraine headaches and epilepsy. Women may experience PMS or endometriosis. Digestive disorders include diabetes, lactose intolerance, colitis, irritable bowel syndrome, and ulcers. Musculoskeletal diseases include arthritis, fibromyalgia, lupus, and chronic low back pain. New chronic health problems such as carpal tunnel syndrome have emerged due to technological advances. Preventive measures for all diseases are recommended.

NAME: _____ DATE: _____

TAKE CHARGE WORKSHEET 14.1

Infection Prevention

DIRECTIONS: Check all of the ways you prevent infection and illness.

_____ Wash your hands with soap and water after using the bathroom.

_____ Wash your hands with soap and water before eating.

_____ Wash your hands with soap and water for at least 15 seconds (long enough to sing "Happy Birthday")

_____ Disinfect bathroom surfaces with cleaning agents or bleach every week.

_____ Disinfect kitchen surfaces with cleaning agents or bleach every week.

_____ Avoid contact with people who cough and sneeze.

_____ Use gloves while cleaning or touching other people's bodily fluids if you have a cut on your hand.

_____ Wash produce from the grocery store before using.

_____ Inspect food for spoilage.

_____ Use different cutting boards for cutting vegetables and meat.

_____ Cook meat thoroughly (no pink inside) to kill any bacteria present.

_____ Do not use cracked eggs for anything.

_____ Do laundry at least once per week (including bed linens and kitchen towels).

_____ Use a dishwasher to sanitize dishes.

_____ Dust and vacuum at least once per week.

_____ Have a special area where pets can eat and sleep.

_____ Have all vaccinations and booster shots up to date.

_____ Avoid contact with bodily fluids from others.

_____ Do not inject or use any type of designer drugs.

_____ Practice safer sex or use a condom.

_____ Do not smoke.

_____ Maintain a healthy weight.

_____ Eat a balanced diet according to the Food Guide Pyramid.

_____ Get at least 6–8 hours sleep per night on a regular basis.

_____ Exercise regularly.

_____ Find relaxing ways to cope with and manage stress.

For Further Thought

Congratulations on the great things you are doing to improve or maintain your health! From the list above, write down the task that you could easily add to your lifestyle that would reduce your chances of getting sick.

NAME: _____ DATE: _____

TAKE CHARGE WORKSHEET 14.2

Myths About Sexually Transmitted Infections

DIRECTIONS: Determine which of the following statements are truths and which are myths. Write *T* next to the statements you think are truths, and *M* next to the statements you think are myths.

_____ 1. You can get a sexually transmitted infection from a toilet seat.

_____ 2. If you wash with soap and water after intercourse, the possibility of a sexually transmitted infection decreases.

_____ 3. Once a rash or a sore heals, it means the infection has cured itself and can not be transmitted to anyone else.

_____ 4. The transmission of a sexually transmitted infection is not possible if a condom is used.

_____ 5. A case of genital warts in a female places her at risk for cervical cancer.

_____ 6. If gonorrhea or chlamydia is left untreated, it can result in pelvic inflammatory disease, and eventual sterility.

_____ 7. HIV is transmitted through blood-to-blood contact.

_____ 8. Symptoms of HIV do not appear until several months or years after infection.

_____ 9. When one partner has a bacterial infection, they do not need to tell the other partner.

_____ 10. Crab lice or scabies can be contracted only by a person from a low socio-economic background.

_____ 11. Most people with a sexually transmitted infection try not to pass it on to someone else.

_____ 12. Campus, city, or county health clinics often treat sexually transmitted infections free or at reduced cost.

_____ 13. College students have a higher risk of contracting a sexually transmitted disease than any other group.

_____ 14. A person under the influence of alcohol is more likely to contract a sexually transmitted infection.

Answers

1. FALSE. Sexually transmitted infections are transmitted from mucosal linings of the mouth, genitals, or rectum. Some infections such as staph infections can be transmitted through contact with an infected object, but toilet seats are not considered "sexual" in nature.

2. TRUE. The possibility of any infection decreases by washing with soap and water, but this does not mean the infection will not manifest itself. It depends on the person's immunity, frequency of contact with an infected individual, and other things that inhibit or encourage the growth of bacteria and viruses.

3. FALSE. Unfortunately, when a sore heals, it does not always mean that the infecting agent is gone. The infection may resurface later when immunity decreases. The individual may also have some skin "shedding" that could transmit the infection.

4. FALSE. A condom is probably the best contraceptive device for preventing a sexually transmitted infection, but it is not foolproof. A condom does not cover all areas that might come in contact with infected skin.

5. TRUE. There does seem to be a correlation between the incidence of genital warts and cervical cancer. Cervical cancer is also associated with multiple sexual partners.

6. TRUE. Certain diseases that are hard to detect in females such as gonorrhea or chlamydia can develop into something more serious if left untreated. Pelvic inflammatory disease is one disease that can cause further complications.

7. TRUE. HIV is transmitted by blood-to-blood contact, but it can also be transmitted through breast milk.

8. TRUE. If a person suspects they may have been exposed to the HIV virus, they can request blood tests, but even a negative test does not mean the HIV virus was not contracted. Sometimes a positive HIV test is not evident until later.

9. FALSE. Most physicians will encourage treatment with antibiotics for both partners so the infection is not transmitted from a healthy person to another. If only one person is treated, then the untreated partner can give it back again.

10. FALSE. Crab lice or scabies are transmitted by skin-to-skin contact or from infested clothing or bedding. Anyone can get it.

11. TRUE. At least we would like to think that most people would not want to give someone else a sexually transmitted infection. However, in the case of any epidemic, there are always a few who refuse to be treated and thus expose many people to the disease.

12. TRUE. There are many clinics that offer free or reduced price services to college students. It would be a good idea if you are sexually active to have an examination and seek other preventative services by calling in advance. Many of these clinics have long waiting lines. A family planning clinic is another option.

13. TRUE. Of all populations studied, college students are most at risk for sexually transmitted infection because of promiscuous behavior. Sexual history of a prospective sexual partner is important information.

14. TRUE. Alcohol affects judgment and lessens normal inhibitions. The incidence of pregnancy and sexually transmitted infection increases when alcohol is consumed. One reason for this is the decreased likelihood that a condom will be used. Alcohol use also increases the likelihood of sexual assault or rape.

NAME: _____ DATE: _____

TAKE CHARGE WORKSHEET 14.3

Should You Have the HIV Test?

DIRECTIONS: Indicate whether or not you have engaged in any of the following behaviors by circling *Yes* or *No*.

Yes No 1. I have had sex without knowing for sure that the person or persons with whom I had sex did not have HIV.

Yes No 2. I have had sex with someone I know has HIV or AIDS.

Yes No 3. I have had a sexually transmitted infection (e.g. syphillis, genital herpes).

Yes No 4. I have had sex with many men/women.

Yes No 5. I have had sex with someone who has had multiple sex partners.

Yes No 6. I have had sex with someone who has used needles to take drugs.

Yes No 7. I have shared needles when taking drugs.

EVALUATION: If you have answered *Yes* to any of these questions, you should think about being tested for HIV.

Source: Adapted from "Should You Have the HIV Test?" How to Help Yourself Series, National Institute of Allergy and Infectious Diseases, National Institutes of Health.

Check Your Asthma I.Q.

DIRECTIONS: The following true or false statements test your knowledge of asthma. Circle your answers and then refer to the Answer section to determine the extent of your knowledge.

True   False   1. Asthma is a common disease among children in the United States.

True   False   2. Asthma is an emotional or psychological illness.

True   False   3. The way parents raise their children can cause asthma.

True   False   4. Asthma episodes may cause breathing problems, but these episodes are not really harmful or dangerous.

True   False   5. Asthma episodes usually occur suddenly and without warning.

True   False   6. Many different things can bring on an asthma episode.

True   False   7. Asthma cannot be cured, but it can be controlled.

True   False   8. There are different types of medicine to control asthma.

True   False   9. People with asthma have no way to monitor how well their lungs are functioning.

True   False   10. Both children and adults can have asthma.

True   False   11. Tobacco smoke can make an asthma episode worse.

True   False   12. People with asthma should not exercise.

Answers

1. TRUE. Asthma is a common disease among children and adults in the United States, and it is increasing. About 10 million people have asthma, of whom 3 million are under 18 years of age.

2. FALSE. Asthma is not an emotional or psychological disease, although strong emotions can sometimes make asthma worse. People with asthma have sensitive lungs that react to certain things, causing airways to tighten, swell, and fill with mucus. The person then has trouble breathing and may cough and wheeze.

3. FALSE. The way parents raise their children does not cause asthma. It is not caused by a poor parent-child relationship or by being overprotective.

4. FALSE. Asthma episodes can be very harmful. People can get very sick and require hospitalization. Some people have died from asthma episodes. Frequent asthma episodes, even if they are mild, may cause people to stop being active and living normal lives.

5. FALSE. Sometimes an asthma episode may come on quite quickly. However, before a person has any wheezing or shortness of breath there are usually symptoms such as a cough, a scratchy

throat, or tightness in the chest. Most patients learn to recognize these early symptoms and can take medicine to prevent a serious episode.

6. TRUE. For most people with asthma, an episode can start from many different "triggers." Some of these things are pollen from trees or grasses; molds or house dust; weather changes; strong odors; cigarette smoke; and certain foods. Other triggers include being upset; laughing or crying hard; having a cold or the flu; or being near furry or feathered animals. Each person with asthma has an individual set of asthma "triggers."

7. TRUE. There is no cure yet for asthma. However, asthma patients can control it to a large degree by:
   a. Getting advice from a doctor who treats asthma patients.
   b. Learning to notice early signs of an asthma episode and to start treatment.
   c. Avoiding things that cause asthma episodes.
   d. Taking medicine according to the prescription.
   e. Knowing when to get medical help during a severe episode.

8. TRUE. Several types of medicines are available to control asthma. Some people with mild asthma need to take medication only when they have symptoms. But most people need to take medicine every day to prevent symptoms and also to take medicine when symptoms do occur. A doctor needs to decide the best type of medicine for each patient and how often it should be taken. Asthma patients and their doctors need to work together to manage the disease.

9. FALSE. People with asthma can monitor how well their lungs are functioning with a peak flow meter. This small device can be used at home, work, or school. The peak flow meter may show that the asthma is getting worse before the usual symptoms appear.

10. TRUE. Both children and adults can have asthma. Sometimes, but not always, symptoms will go away as children get older. However, many children continue to have asthma symptoms throughout adulthood. In some cases, symptoms of asthma are not recognized until a person is an adult.

11. TRUE. Smoke from cigarettes, cigars, and pipes can bring on an asthma attack. Indoor smoky air from fireplaces and outdoor smog can make asthma worse. Some can also "set off" other triggers. Smokers should be asked not to smoke near someone with asthma. Moving to another room may help, but smoke travels from room to room. No smoking is best for everyone!

12. FALSE. Exercise is good for most people—with or without asthma. When asthma is under control, people with asthma are able to play most sports. For people whose asthma is brought on by exercise, medicines can be taken before exercising to help avoid an episode. A number of Olympic athletes have asthma.

EVALUATION:

11–12 Correct = Congratulations! You know a lot about asthma. Share this information with your family and friends.

10–11 Correct = Very good.

Fewer than 10 correct = Go over the answers and try to learn more about asthma.

Source: Check Your Asthma I.Q., National Asthma Education Program, National Heart, Lung and Blood Institute, National Institutes of Health, Reprinted October 1992.

General Review Questions

1. Summarize the body's defenses against disease-causing pathogens.

2. Distinguish between acquired immunity and natural immunity.

3. List and give an example of the major types of pathogens.

4. What are the routes of disease transmission?

5. Explain how HIV is transmitted.

Practice Test 1

1. Organisms that normally coexist with human hosts and are usually harmless are called:

   a. pathogens.

   b. exogenous microorganisms.

   c. endogenous microorganisms.

   d. infections microorganisms.

2. Which of the following is a *bacterial* disorder?

   a. hepatitis

   b. measles

   c. mononucleosis

   d. toxic shock syndrome

3. The smallest of the pathogens is:

   a. prions.

   b. virus.

   c. protozoa.

   d. bacteria.

4. What inherited blood disease primarily affects African Americans and results in organ damage and premature death?

   a. AIDS

   b. sickle cell anemia

   c. diabetes

   d. muscular dystrophy

5. What is the single greatest factor influencing your longevity?

   a. gender

   b. socioeconomic status

   c. parents' longevity

   d. marital status

6. A respiratory disease in which the alveoli of the lungs are gradually destroyed is known as:

   a. asthma.

   b. hay fever.

   c. emphysema.

   d. chronic bronchitis.

7. Epilepsy is:

   a. a localized headache on only one side of the head.

   b. a neurological disorder caused by abnormal electrical brain activity.

   c. characterized by excruciating pain that lasts for minutes or hours.

   d. a hereditary disease that is more common in women than men.

8. Dengue viruses are transmitted by

   a. E. coli.

   b. rodent feces.

   c. mosquitoes.

   d. infected cows.

9. Symptoms for diabetes include all of the following, *except*:

   a. excessive thirst.

   b. hypoglycemia.

   c. frequent urination.

   d. skin eruptions.

10. What is a common occupational injury associated with typing on the computer?

    a. carpal tunnel syndrome

    b. chronic fatigue syndrome

    c. chronic Epstein Barr disease

    d. seasonal affective disorder

11. Chemical substances that dilate blood vessels, increase mucous secretions, cause tissues to swell, and produce other allergy-like symptoms are called:

    a. allergens.

    b. antibodies.

    c. histamines.

    d. antigens.

12. Henry suffers from 15 bouts of diarrhea a day, weight loss, nausea, sweating, and fever. What disorder does he most likely have?

    a. peptic ulcers

    b. ulcerative colitis

    c. diverticulosis

    d. Raynaud's syndrome

13. A seizure disorder characterized by an absence of convulsions, minor loss of consciousness that may go unnoticed, and a minor twitching of muscles is called:

    a. Jacksonian seizure.

    b. grand mal seizure.

    c. petit mal seizure.

    d. psychomotor seizure.

14. The Western blot is a test used to detect the presence of

    a. hepatitis.

    b. syphilis.

    c. chlamydia.

    d. HIV antibodies.

15. All of the following are common treatments for PMS, *except*:

    a. aspirin.

    b. stress reduction techniques.

    c. exercise.

    d. decreased intake of complex carbohydrates.

Practice Test 2

1. During what stage of syphilis does a chancre develop?

    a. primary syphilis

    b. secondary syphilis

    c. latent syphilis

    d. late syphilis

2. Cocci, bacilli, and spirilla are three major types of:

    a. antibodies.

    b. viruses.

    c. bacteria.

    d. microorganisms.

3. A viral disease that causes inflammation of the liver is called:

    a. hepatitis.

    b. herpes simplex.

    c. AIDS.

    d. measles.

4. Single-celled organisms that cause diseases such as trichomoniasis and giardiasis are called:

    a. fungi.

    b. bacteria.

    c. rickettsia.

    d. protozoa.

5. Which of the following infections is caused by fungi?

    a. ringworm

    b. trichomoniasis

    c. rabies

    d. pneumonia

6. Which of the following is a *viral* disorder?

    a. measles

    b. pneumonia

    c. tuberculosis

    d. streptococcal infections

7. Which of the following is an autoimmune disorder?

    a. tuberculosis

    b. hepatitis

    c. lupus erythematosus

    d. pneumonia

8. Sleep apnea affects what percent of the general population?

    a. 1 percent

    b. 5 percent

    c. 10 percent

    d. 20 percent

9. A chronic respiratory disease characterized by attacks of wheezing, shortness of breath, and coughing spasms is called:

a. allergies.

b. asthma.

c. emphysema.

d. chronic bronchitis.

10. What is a major risk factor for chronic bronchitis?

a. ragweed and pollen

b. use of cigarettes

c. animal dander

d. dust

11. What degenerative disease involves the breakdown of myelin?

a. epilepsy

b. multiple sclerosis

c. cerebral palsy

d. Parkinson's disease

12. What sexually transmitted infection has as its main symptom a white milky discharge from the penis accompanied by painful, burning urination?

a. chlamydia

b. syphilis

c. gonorrhea

d. pelvic inflammatory disease

13. Deb has a headache that is localized on one side of the head. What type of headache does she most likely have?

a. tension

b. migraine

c. secondary

d. psychosomatic

14. Chris has progressive seizures that typically begin in his fingers and then move to his arm, usually affecting only his right side. What type of seizure disorder does he have?

a. petit mal

b. grand mal

c. Jacksonian

d. psychomotor

15. What condition is believed to have strong psychosocial roots in the absence of a known pathogen?

a. scleroderma

b. Raynaud's syndrome

c. chronic fatigue syndrome

d. systemic lupus erythematosus

15

Life's Transitions

Chapter Overview

Biological age, psychological age, social age, legal age, and functional age are all considered when determining the extent of aging. Many older adults are active and productive because they have escaped serious disease and disability and maintain a high level of physical functioning. They remain mentally active by engaging in challenging and stimulating activities, participating in social events, and being productive. Resiliency and ability to cope are important factors for "aging gracefully."

There are three categories, defined by specific age-related characteristics, within the aging process. People between 65 and 74 years of age are now called the *young-old*, those between 75 and 84 are called the *middle-old*, and those 85 and over are the *old-old* group. The number of older Americans has increased more than ten times since 1900. Health care costs for the elderly have risen by 33% since 1990. Five percent of older Americans now live in nursing homes.

The *wear-and-tear theory* of aging suggests that we "wear out," just like everything else in the universe. The *cellular theory* suggests that cells die when they reach the end of their reproductive cycle. The *autoimmune theory* attributes aging to a declining immune system. The *genetic mutation* theory proposes that cells mutate or change as a person ages. Physical changes with aging include thinner, less elastic skin, redistribution of body fat, the effects of sun exposure become more noticeable, bones change, facial features appear larger, and the skull thickens while the brain grows smaller. The kidneys become less efficient and the bladder shrinks, making incontinence a common, though not inevitable, problem. The heart and lungs become less efficient and sensitivity to heat and cold increases. Most individuals will develop vision or hearing problems. Sexual functioning varies greatly for men and women, but many older people remain sexually active. Mental changes can include a decrease in short-term memory, depression, senility, and Alzheimer's disease. Many older adults take several medications, and negative drug interactions and other problems may result. Many people prefer to avoid traditional medical treatment if over-the-counter medications and other alternatives are available.

The body is designed to last for many years, provided it is not abused. It is important to develop a healthy lifestyle early in life and continue to maintain good health. Strategies include developing and maintaining healthy relationships, expanding the spiritual aspects of health, daily exercise, and healthy eating.

The process of dying has five predictable, psychological stages that people often experience. The first stage is denial, followed by anger, and then bargaining. Depression and acceptance complete the stages. Patterns vary from person to person.

The right to die and rational suicide are issues that have been intensely debated in recent years. Living wills have emerged to resolve conflicts that arise when an individual does not wish to be resuscitated or kept alive by artificial means. In order to ease the trauma of losing a loved one, it is important to make plans for long-term or hospice care, funeral arrangements, to create a will, and to decide whether or not to be an organ donor. Hospice programs assist a dying person with pain and provide emotional support to the dying person and loved ones. Making these decisions in advance will help make a difficult time a little easier for surviving friends and family members.

NAME: _____ DATE: _____

TAKE CHARGE WORKSHEET 15.1

Attitudes Toward Older Adults

DIRECTIONS: Check the items that you think are true. Share some of your impressions with others in your class.

_____ 1. All individuals over the age of 65 should be considered *elderly*.

_____ 2. I don't think that older people should get "early bird specials" or discounts just because they are older.

_____ 3. If a person was irritable and hostile throughout most of their life, then they probably will be irritable and hostile when they are older.

_____ 4. Most older Americans will fall, break something, and end up in a nursing home.

_____ 5. Older people who drive should be considered high-risk drivers.

_____ 6. Older people are not as effective at work as younger people.

_____ 7. The older you get, the more "set in your ways" you become.

_____ 8. As we get older, our reaction time decreases due to poor vision and physical condition.

_____ 9. Most elderly people are hard of hearing.

_____ 10. Older people do not have to feel lonely or isolated when there are programs like "meals on wheels" and senior dining centers.

_____ 11. When I get old, I want to play bingo.

_____ 12. When Generation X retires, there will be no money left to collect Social Security from the government.

_____ 13. It is not necessary to save for retirement until after your children have grown and moved out of the home.

_____ 14. If an older person needs something to do, they should volunteer their time rather than take paying jobs away from younger people.

_____ 15. I do not have to worry about my spiritual growth until I am older and closer to death.

NAME: _____ DATE: _____

TAKE CHARGE WORKSHEET 15.2

Ten Ways to Recognize Hearing Loss

DIRECTIONS: Place a checkmark by the symptoms and risk factors associated with hearing loss that are applicable to you.

_____ I listen to loud music in my car.

_____ I usually have the stereo turned up so loud that the neighbors complain.

_____ I work in an area where the noise is so loud that I should probably wear ear plugs.

_____ I enjoy going to clubs or concerts where the music is very loud.

_____ Sometimes, after I listen to loud music, sounds are muffled, but it goes away.

_____ If I sit at the back of a classroom, I have a hard time understanding what the teacher and classmates say.

_____ Sometimes I have to look at a person's lips to be sure I don't miss anything they say.

_____ I get aggravated when people mumble and I don't know what they have said.

_____ Sometimes people have to get my attention before I notice that they are talking.

_____ Lately, I've had to ask people to repeat what they said because I couldn't hear all of it.

_____ There have been times when I thought I knew what someone said, but I realized later that I didn't get the message.

_____ People who are close to me get annoyed with me because I ask them to repeat what they said.

_____ If there is some type of background noise, it's always harder for me to hear what is said.

_____ I have never had a hearing test.

_____ I had frequent ear infections as a child.

For Further Thought

Carefully look at the statements that you have checked. If you think you may have a hearing problem, it would be a good idea to talk to your doctor, an audiologist, or an ear, nose, and throat (otolaryngologist) specialist about a hearing test.

NAME: _____ DATE: _____

TAKE CHARGE WORKSHEET 15.3

Thinking About Life and Death

DIRECTIONS: In order to live a better life, we sometimes need to take an inventory or analyze our current life and make changes. Answer each of the statements below to determine the areas of your life that you might need to change.

1. List 5–6 people close to your age with whom you would like to spend more time than you do right now. Include some of the things you would like to do with them.

2. List 3–4 people who are older than you with whom you would like to spend more time.

3. List 3–4 people who are younger than you with whom you would like to spend more time.

4. Of the people you have listed above, write the names of 3 people you think will die first.

5. List 5–6 of your most prized possessions.

6. If you were to die in the near future, who would you like to have those possessions?

7. If you were to die in the near future, what other arrangements would you want to make?

8. Would you consider donating your organs? Why or why not?

9. Would you want to have a living will? Why or why not?

10. What, if any, religious preference would you claim and would you like a religious person to help you and the family through the dying and grief process?

11. How much money would you want to spend on your funeral arrangements?

12. Would you like to have a viewing, memorial service, funeral, burial, or cremation? Explain your answer.

13. If you were no longer living, what would you want people to say about you?

14. How could you change your life, right now, to make your life experience more memorable, positive, or fulfilling?

NAME: _____ DATE: _____

Dealing with Death

DIRECTIONS: Reflect on your past experiences with death while answering the following questions below.

1. What was your first experience with death?

2. How old were you?

3. How did you feel about seeing a deceased pet, friend, or relative?

4. What was your reaction when you learned of the death?

5. How did others react to the death?

6. Was there a viewing of the body or a family gathering before or after a memorial service?

7. What methods did you use to cope with the death when you were sad?

8. How long do you think the grief process took before you felt better?

9. Was there anything that could have been done to make the grief process less painful?

10. When someone you know loses someone they love to a death, what do you say?

11. When someone you know loses someone they love to death, what do you do to help?

12. Do you think the type or sudden nature of death has an impact on your ability to cope with a death?

NAME: _____ DATE: _____

TAKE CHARGE WORKSHEET 15.5

Eye-Q Test

Fifty million Americans are at risk for vision loss from glaucoma, a leading cause of blindness in the United States. Are you one of them? If you are, do you know how to reduce your risk of blindness?

DIRECTIONS: To determine how high your "Eye-Q" is, answer the following questions about glaucoma. Answers are found on the back of this worksheet.

True   False   1. Glaucoma is more common in blacks than in whites.

True   False   2. Glaucoma tends to run in families.

True   False   3. A person can have glaucoma and not know it.

True   False   4. People over age 60 are more likely to get glaucoma.

True   False   5. Eye pain is often a symptom of glaucoma.

True   False   6. Glaucoma can be controlled.

True   False   7. Glaucoma is caused by increased eye pressure.

True   False   8. Vision lost from glaucoma can be restored.

True   False   9. A complete glaucoma exam consists only of measuring eye pressure.

True   False   10. People at risk for glaucoma should have an eye examination through dilated pupils.

Answers

1. TRUE. In a study funded by the National Eye Institute, researchers at The Johns Hopkins University reported that glaucoma is three to four times more likely to occur in blacks than in whites. In addition, glaucoma is six times more likely to cause blindness in blacks than in whites.

2. TRUE. Although glaucoma tends to run in families, a hereditary basis has not been established. If someone in your immediate family has glaucoma, you should have your eyes examined through dilated pupils at least every two years.

3. TRUE. The early stages of open-angle glaucoma, the most common form, usually has no warning signs. However, as the disease progresses, a person with glaucoma may notice his or her side vision gradually failing.

4. TRUE. Everyone over age 60 has an increased risk for glaucoma. Other groups at increased risk include blacks over age 40 and people with a family history of the disease.

5. FALSE. People with glaucoma usually do not experience pain from the disease.

6. TRUE. Although glaucoma cannot be cured, it usually can be controlled by eye drops or pills, conventional surgery, or laser surgery. Sometimes eye care professionals will recommend a combination of surgery and medication.

7. TRUE. In glaucoma, for reasons still not completely understood, fluid drains too slowly out of the eye. As the fluid builds up, the pressure inside the eye rises. Unless this pressure is controlled, it may cause damage to the optic nerve and other parts of the eye and loss of vision.

8. FALSE. Vision loss from glaucoma is permanent. However, with early detection and treatment, the progression of visual loss can be slowed, or halted, and the risk of blindess reduced.

9. FALSE. A measurement of eye pressure by tonometry, though an important part of a comprehensive eye examination, is by itself not sufficient for the detection of glaucoma. Glaucoma is detected most often during an eye examination through dilated pupils. This means drops are put into the eyes during the examination to enlarge the pupils, which allows the eye care professional to see more of the inside of the eye to check for signs of glaucoma. When indicated, a visual field test should be performed.

10. TRUE. An eye examination through dilated pupils is the best way to diagnose glaucoma. Individuals at increased risk for the disease should have their eyes examined through dilated pupils at least every two years by an eye care professional.

EVALUATION: If you got 9 or 10 right, congratulations! You know a lot about glaucoma. If you missed some, review the answers so you can share your knowledge with your family and friends.

Source: National Eye Health Education Program, National Eye Institute, National Institutes of Health, Revised 8-99.

General Review Questions

1. List the different ways to define age.

2. What are the characteristics of people who have aged successfully?

3. What are five psychological stages that terminally ill patients often experience as they approach death?

4. Distinguish between active euthanasia and passive euthanasia.

5. What are the primary goals of hospice programs?

Practice Test 1

1. According to Erik Erikson,
   a. people must progress through eight critical stages in their lifetime.
   b. painful aging is caused by a lack of appropriate coping skills.
   c. aging is related to the amount of mutational damage within the genes.
   d. as we age, our immune system becomes more effective in fighting disease.

2. Your habits and roles relative to society's expectations define your:
   a. functional age.
   b. psychological age.
   c. legal age.
   d. social age.

3. A disease that breaks down the light-sensitive part of the retina responsible for sharp, direct vision is called
   a. glaucoma.
   b. cataracts.
   c. osteoporosis.
   d. macular degeneration.

4. What is the most common form of dementia in older adults?

   a. Alzheimer's disease

   b. incontinence

   c. depression

   d. psychosis

5. The "young-old" are people who are:

   a. 55–64 years of age.

   b. 65–74 years of age.

   c. 75–84 years of age.

   d. 85 years or older.

6. According to cellular theory, aging is caused by:

   a. the human body wearing out.

   b. the body's cells having reached the end of their reproductive cycle.

   c. the decline of the body's immunological system.

   d. an increased number of cells exhibiting unusual or different characteristics with increased age.

7. A clouding of the eye lens is called:

   a. cataracts.

   b. glaucoma.

   c. color blindness.

   d. astigmatism.

8. Mary's grandfather has been diagnosed with Alzheimer's disease. She observes that he is quite agitated and restless and has experienced a loss of sensory perceptions. He has become more depressed lately and repeats many behaviors. What stage of Alzheimer's is he in?

   a. first

   b. second

   c. third

   d. fourth

9. Which of the following symptoms characterize the first stage of Alzheimer's disease?

   a. identity loss and speech problems

   b. forgetfulness, impaired judgment, depression

   c. loss of sensory perceptions, muscle twitching, and repetitive actions

   d. total dependence on others for eating, dressing, and other activities

10. The stage of grief that is characterized by the dying person resolving to be a better person in return for an extension of life is called:

    a. denial.

    b. anger.

    c. bargaining.

    d. depression.

11. On average, patients with Alzheimer's disease live for

    a. 6 months to a year after diagnosis.

    b. 2 to 5 years after diagnosis.

    c. 8 to 10 years after diagnosis.

    d. 10–15 years after diagnosis.

12. What is the first psychological stage that terminally ill patients often experience as they approach death?

    a. anger

    b. denial

    c. depression

    d. bargaining

13. Extramarital lovers who find it difficult to mourn the death of their lover because of societal stigmas may experience:

    a. bereavement.

    b. bereavement displacement.

    c. disenfranchised grief.

    d. denial.

14. Saul has experienced many losses in his life, including the loss of his wife, friends, and children. His gloomy outlook and disturbing behavior patterns may be symptomatic of:

a. an age-associated dementia.

b. self-pity.

c. bereavement overload.

d. depression.

15. A concept of care for terminally ill patients designed to maximize quality of life is called:

a. hospice.

b. respite care.

c. gerontology.

d. thanatology.

Practice Test 2

1. What definition of age is used as a factor in determining voting rights?

a. social

b. legal

c. biological

d. functional

2. What is the most common definition of age in the United States?

a. legal age

b. social age

c. biological age

d. functional age

3. According to the autoimmune theory, aging is caused by:

a. the human body wearing out.

b. the body's cells having reached the end of their reproductive cycle.

c. the decline of the body's immunological system.

d. an increased number of cells exhibiting unusual or different characteristics with increased age.

4. Walt's opthamologist tells him that there is an elevation of pressure within his eyeball. What is this condition?

a. cataracts

b. glaucoma

c. far-sightedness

d. near-sightedness

5. The form of "mercy killing" in which life-prolonging treatments or interventions are not offered or withheld, thereby allowing a terminally ill person to die naturally, is called:

a. suicide.

b. euthanasia.

c. dyathanasia.

d. self-deliverance.

6. The study of death and dying is called:

a. thanatology.

b. gerontology.

c. ageism.

d. senescence.

7. The "middle-old" are people who are
   a. 55–64 years of age.
   b. 65–74 years of age.
   c. 75–84 years of age.
   d. 85 years and older.

8. Mourning is:
   a. the loss or deprivation experienced by a survivor when a loved one dies.
   b. the effects of multiple losses and the accumulation of sorrow in the lives of some elderly people.
   c. culturally prescribed and accepted time periods and behavior patterns for the expression of grief.
   d. when a person experiences a loss that cannot be openly acknowledged, publicly acknowledged, or socially supported.

9. What theory proposes that the number of cells exhibiting unusual or different characteristics increases with age?
   a. wear-and-tear theory
   b. cellular theory
   c. autoimmune theory
   d. genetic mutation theory

10. After her husband died, Sue experienced a loss of appetite, an inability to sleep at night, and inability to concentrate. She is experiencing:
    a. grief.
    b. denial.
    c. mourning.
    d. bereavement.

11. Grief work is:
    a. the process of integrating the reality of the loss with everyday life and learning to feel better.
    b. the total acceptance that a loved one has died.
    c. assigning feelings to the loss of a loved one.
    d. completing the cultural rituals that are required to express one's grief.

12. What degenerative bone disorder is characterized by increasingly porous bones?
    a. osteoporosis
    b. diabetes
    c. arthritis
    d. dementia

13. A will written in the testator's own handwriting and unwitnessed is called a(n):
    a. donor's will.
    b. living will.
    c. intestate will.
    d. holographic will.

14. Dying intestate means that an individual has died:
    a. in a state other than where he resides.
    b. without leaving a will.
    c. without prearranging a funeral.
    d. with a living will.

15. Kerri's elderly grandmother is terminally ill and wants to die without receiving medical intervention. Her family has agreed to withhold treatment that may prolong her life. This is called:
    a. rational suicide.
    b. self-deliverance.
    c. passive euthanasia.
    d. active euthanasia.

16

Environmental Health

Chapter Overview

Global population growth is a threat to environmental health. Countries are becoming overpopulated, creating increased demands on the Earth's resources. As the global population rises, we face greater environmental issues. Efforts have been taken to limit population growth in some countries, but the problem is far from stabilized.

Photochemical smog, acid rain, the greenhouse effect, and the depletion of the ozone layer are all problems related to air pollution. Since the 1970s, laws have been enacted to limit air pollution, but it continues to be a problem. Sulfur dioxide, particulate matter, carbon monoxide, ozone, nitrogen dioxide, lead, and hydrocarbons can be found in the air, particularly around industrial sites or in large communities. You may see photochemical smog as it forms when vehicle exhaust reacts with sunlight, giving the air a brown, hazy color. Smog creates and worsens respiratory problems among children, the elderly, pregnant women, and people with chronic lung disease. Acid rain results when pollutants in the air make the rain more acidic, ruining plant and animal life. Many of us live in indoor environments polluted by wood stove smoke, improper furnace maintenance, asbestos, formaldehyde, radon, and household chemicals. The ozone layer is thinning, which increases the risk of skin cancers. In addition, average global temperatures are higher today than at any time in history due to the greenhouse effect. Measures to reduce air pollution include more efficient fuel emission systems on cars, and encouragement of commuters to car pool, bicycle, or use mass transit transportation systems.

While most of us take drinking water for granted, in many parts of the world it is undrinkable. Water becomes polluted when sedimentation and other pollutants leak into a water source. Some of the pollutants come from soil erosion, construction waste, fertilizers, street runoff, engineering waste, mine drainage, leakage from septic tanks and sewage systems, or leachate from landfills. Petroleum products and solvents from cleaning products, which are highly toxic, have been found in water supplies. PCBs, dioxins, pesticides, and lead are especially harmful to the water supply.

Noise pollution is also of increasing concern lately, particularly since hearing decreases as we age. Prolonged exposure to high decibels will cause hearing loss. Keeping noise down and wearing ear plugs when operating power equipment are good precautionary measures.

Waste management is becoming an increasingly important issue as available land for waste disposal is becoming increasingly scarce and many of the products we use are disposable. Approximately 90% of our trash is recyclable, however, and increased recycling could help lessen the waste management problem.

Fifty percent of our exposure to radiation comes from natural sources, 45% comes from medical and dental X-rays, and the remaining 5% comes from computer screens, microwaves, television sets, luminous watch dials, and radar. Electromagnetic fields are believed to be harmful, but the evidence is inconclusive. Nuclear energy is an important fuel source because it is less expensive and more efficient. Nuclear reactors discharge fewer pollutants in the air than fossil-fuel–powered generators. Radioactive waste disposal remains a problem. It is known that health problems can occur as a result of the disposal of radioactive waste. In 1980, Superfund legislation was enacted to clean up chemical dump areas that endanger health. Over 32,500 hazardous waste sites have been identified, and 1,300 sites are still on the National Priorities List.

NAME: _____ DATE: _____

TAKE CHARGE WORKSHEET 16.1

Living Simply

DIRECTIONS: The twentieth century was a century of materialism. Buy! Buy bigger! Buy more! Supersize! What will the twenty-first century look like? How will you contribute to caring for your environment? Answer the following questions to reflect on your personal responsibility for the environment.

1. Are my environmental values reflected in the way I care for my home, my family, my friends, and my work?

2. How do I contribute to pollution? What steps can I take to begin caring for my environment?

3. What environmental issues is Congress facing? Do I contact those in political power to inform them of my position?

4. What one environmental issue am I most concerned about? (Some examples are: clean water, energy, forests, wildlands.) How can I make a contribution to this environmental cause to protect future generations?

For Further Thought

Visit the following websites to learn more about how to contribute to environmental health:

http://www.niehs.nih.gov/
National Institute of Environmental Health Sciences (NIEHS)

http://www.cdc.gov/nceh/
National Center for Environmental Health

http://www.neha.org/
National Environmental Health Association

http://www.simpleliving.net/
The Simple Living Network

http://www.sierraclub.org/politics/
The Sierra Club

TAKE CHARGE WORKSHEET 16.2

Air Pollution Quiz

DIRECTIONS: Place the answer you think is correct in the space provided next to the question.

_____ 1. Sources of indoor pollution can come from:

    a. carpeting.

    b. paint.

    c. dust.

    d. all of the above.

_____ 2. Radon is most often found:

    a. in kitchens.

    b. in basements.

    c. in attics.

    d. in bathrooms.

_____ 3. The primary source of carbon monoxide poisoning in the home is:

    a. not shutting off the gas stove completely.

    b. a fireplace.

    c. a malfunctioning furnace.

    d. an attached garage.

_____ 4. A sick building is detected when symptoms occur among workers or residents as a result of:

    a. uncontrolled mold and mildew.

    b. inadequate ventilation system.

    c. uncontrolled dust particles.

    d. all of the above.

_____ 5. The primary source of outdoor air pollution is:

    a. manufacturing plants.

    b. automobile exhaust.

    c. waste given off as plants deteriorate and rot.

    d. thermal inversion.

_____ 6. Which of the following are caused by air pollution?

    a. greenhouse effect

    b. thinning of the ozone layer

    c. global warming

    d. all of the above

_____ 7. Which fuel gives off the least amount of air pollutants?

    a. nuclear

    b. coal

    c. steam

    d. oil

_____ 8. Which is the most harmful substance emitted when something burns?

    a. carbon dioxide

    b. sulphuric acid

    c. carbon monoxide

    d. nitrous oxide

Answers

1. d. all of the above
2. b. in basements
3. c. a malfunctioning furnace
4. d. all of the above
5. b. automobile exhaust
6. d. all of the above
7. a. nuclear
8. c. carbon monoxide

NAME: _____ DATE: _____

TAKE CHARGE WORKSHEET 16.3

Reduce, Reuse, Recycle

DIRECTIONS: Select the things you can do to decrease the amount of trash you contribute to the landfills.

Reduce

_____ Purchase products that have refills that you can buy.

_____ Avoid purchasing products packaged in styrofoam.

_____ Avoid purchasing drinks in paper or plastic cups that are used once and thrown away.

_____ Buy products wrapped in plastic wrap rather than plastic boxes.

_____ Avoid purchasing products that are individually wrapped.

_____ Use household products for cleaning instead of buying corrosive chemicals in spray bottles.

_____ Visit a "green" store in your area.

Reuse

_____ Refill spray bottles, laundry detergent, or fabric softener bottles rather than buying new items.

_____ Think of creative ways to reduce plastic containers.

_____ Use plastic or ceramic plates rather than paper plates.

_____ Use cloth napkins rather than paper napkins.

_____ Use old clothing for cleaning rags.

Recycle

_____ Save and bundle newspapers (excluding colored pages).

_____ Recycle scrap paper at work.

_____ Rinse out, remove labels, and save tin cans.

_____ Rinse out plastic containers and sort by number (#1, #2, and #3 are recyclable).

_____ Rinse out milk containers.

_____ Rinse out and save glass bottles.

_____ Sort paper, tin, aluminum, plastic, and glass in separate containers.

_____ Take recyclable items to the nearest recycling center.

_____ Place vegetable matter from the kitchen and yard in a compost pile.

_____ Water the compost pile once per week.

For Further Thought

Use the space below to list other things you can do to reduce expenses and trash.

NAME: _____ DATE: _____

Environmentally Friendly Cleaning Products

DIRECTIONS: Try making and using some of the cleaning products below from household ingredients.

Drain Cleaner

1 cup salt

1 cup soda

Mix together and pour down the drain. Add 1 cup vinegar. Pour 2 quarts boiling water over all.

Window Cleaner

1/4 cup rubbing alcohol

1 tsp. ammonia

1 tsp. liquid detergent

1 gallon water

Blue food coloring (optional)

Mix together.

Furniture Polish

2 cups mineral oil

6 drops lemon extract (optional)

Put in spray bottle, shake, and spray.

NAME: _____ DATE: _____

TAKE CHARGE WORKSHEET 16.5

Checklist for the Prevention of Carbon Monoxide (CO) Poisoning

DIRECTIONS: The following questions relating to various areas in your environment will help you in dealing properly with the unseen, deadly hazard of carbon monoxide. The questions have been divided into sections that may directly apply to your particular situation. Most questions will apply equally to homeowners, campers, and to those who rent. Renters, however, should refer to the management any questions regarding maintenance. Draw a circle around your answer.

Yes   No   1. Have you had the fireplace draft and the drafts of other fuel-burning appliances checked by an expert within the past year?

Yes   No   2. Have all gas appliances been checked annually for proper operation?

Yes   No   3. Are all combustion appliances properly vented?

Yes   No   4. Has your chimney vent been checked for defects within the past year?

Yes   No   5. Have you patched any vent pipe with tape, gum, or other substances?

Yes   No   6. Are all horizontal vent pipes to fuel appliances perfectly level?

Yes   No   7. Do you use your gas range or oven for heating?

Yes   No   8. Does the cooling unit of your gas refrigerator give off an odor?

Yes   No   9. Have you ever used a charcoal grill, such as a barbecue grill, for cooking within your home, cabin, or camper, other than in a vented fireplace?

Yes   No   10. Have you ever brought burning charcoal into your home, cabin, or camper for heating purposes?

Yes   No   11. Do you consider portable flameless chemical heaters (catalytic) safe for use in your cabin, camper, or home?

Yes   No   12. Have you ever used a portable gas camp stove in your home, cabin, or camper for heating purposes?

Yes   No   13. Have you had a reliable mechanic check the exhaust system of your car within the past year?

Yes   No   14. Do you ever run your auto engine in the garage while the garage door is shut?

Yes   No   15. Do you leave the door closed between your attached garage and your house when you run your car engine?

Yes No 16. Do you keep your windows slightly open while driving in heavy traffic, although you have an air conditioner?

Yes No 17. While driving your station wagon, do you lower the tailgate to get a greater flow of air in the car?

Yes No 18. When you are selecting gas equipment, do you buy only those items that carry the seal of a national testing agency, such as the American Gas Association or the Underwriters' Laboratory?

Yes No 19. Have you ever converted, or are you about to convert, a fuel burner from one fuel to another without having it done by an expert?

Yes No 20. As an overnight guest at motels or hotels that have heating units located in the room, do you read operating instructions or ask how such appliances operate?

Answers

1. Yes. A yearly check up of all fuel-burning venting systems in the home is desirable.

2. Yes. A yearly check up of all combustion appliances is suggested. In many areas, upon request, the gas company will provide this service.

3. Yes. All gas appliances must have adequate ventilation so that CO will not accumulate.

4. Yes. Chimney vents often become blocked by debris, causing a buildup of CO. They should be checked annually.

5. No. Often a makeshift patch can lead to an accumulation of CO, and therefore should be avoided.

6. No. In-room vent pipes should be on a slight incline as they go toward the exterior. This will reduce leaking of toxic gases in case the joints or pipes are improperly fitted.

7. No. Using a gas range for heating can result in the accumulation of CO.

8. No. An unusual odor from a gas refrigerator often is the result of defects within the cooling unit.

9. No. The use of barbecue grills indoors will quickly result in dangerous levels of CO.

10. No. Burning charcoal—whether black, red, gray, or white—gives off CO.

11. No. Although catalytic heaters produce heat without flame, combustion is occurring that can cause the production of CO.

12. No. Using a gas camp stove for heating the home, cabin, or camper results in the accumulation of CO.

13. Yes. Small leaks in the exhaust system of a car can lead to an accumulation of CO.

14. No. CO can rapidly build up while your auto engine is operated in a closed garage. Never run your car in a garage unless the outside door is open to provide ventilation.

15. Yes. CO can easily escape from a garage through a connecting door that opens into the house, although the garage door is open. Doors connecting a garage and house should be kept closed when the auto is running.

16. Yes. Even with an air conditioner, CO can be drawn into a car while it is being driven slowly in heavy traffic. Therefore, windows should be slightly opened.

17. No. If the tailgate is open, be sure to open vents or windows to increase the flow of air into the car. If the tailgate window is open and the other windows or the vents are closed, CO from the exhaust will be drawn into the car.

18. Yes. Buy only equipment carrying the seal of a national testing agency; otherwise one may get poorly designed equipment, which may soon result in the production of CO.

19. No. An expert is needed to make proper modifications and to evaluate the venting capabilities of your appliance.

20. Yes. Even with adequately designed and properly installed heating equipment, the improper operation of this equipment can result in its malfunctioning and lead to the production of CO. Therefore, be sure you understand the correct way to operate any fuel-burning appliance before using it.

EVALUATION: Give yourself one point for each correct answer. A score of 20 points indicates that you have taken the most precautions to prevent carbon monoxide poinsoning. A score of less than 20 points indicates you may need to take action to prevent CO poisoning from some unknown sources.

Source: Centers for Disease Control

General Review Questions

1. Explain how the ozone layer is being depleted.

2. What are two general sources of water pollution?

3. What are the most widespread air pollutants that seriously affect health?

4. Discuss the major sources of chemical contamination.

5. Review the advantages and disadvantages of nuclear power plants.

Practice Test 1

1. The terms *point source* and *nonpoint source* are used to describe the two general sources of

   a. water pollution.

   b. air pollution.

   c. noise pollution.

   d. ozone depletion.

2. The vast bulk of population growth in developing countries is occurring in:

   a. rural areas.

   b. urban areas.

   c. suburban areas.

   d. undeveloped areas.

3. Jason and Elaine believe in the concept of zero population growth, so they decide to limit their offspring to:

   a. 0.

   b. 1.

   c. 2.

   d. 3.

4. What country is projected to have the largest increase in population?

   a. India

   b. China

   c. United States

   d. Zimbabwe

5. What is the term for a weather condition that occurs when a layer of cool air is trapped under a layer of warmer air and prevents the air from circulating?

   a. greenhouse effect

   b. ozone

   c. temperature inversion

   d. photochemical smog

6. Precipitation that has fallen through acidic air pollutants, particularly those containing sulfur dioxides and nitrogen dioxides, is known as:

   a. ozone.

   b. acid rain.

   c. photochemical smog.

   d. temperature inversion.

7. What substance separates into stringy fibers, embeds in lungs, and causes mesothelioma?

   a. asbestos

   b. particulate matter

   c. radon

   d. formaldehyde

8. What percent of a building's occupants must report problems for sick building syndrome to exist?

   a. 33 percent

   b. 50 percent

   c. 66 percent

   d. 80 percent

9. How much of the earth is covered with water?

   a. 15 percent

   b. 45 percent

   c. 60 percent

   d. 75 percent

10. Cigarette smoke releases what air pollutant?

    a. particulates

    b. sulfur dioxide

    c. nitrogen dioxide

    d. hydrocarbons

11. What gas is formed when nitrogen dioxide interacts with hydrogen chloride?

    a. ozone

    b. carbon monoxide

    c. sulfur dioxide

    d. particulates

12. What is the recommended maximum "safe" dosage of radiation?

    a. 0.5 rads to 5 rads per year

    b. 2.5 rads to 35 rads per year

    c. 50 rads to 60 rads per year

    d. 100 rads to 200 rads per year

13. Radiation caused by the release of particles and electromagnetic rays from atomic nuclei during the normal process of disintegration is called:

    a. radioactive emissions.

    b. nuclear energy.

    c. fission.

    d. ionizing radiation.

14. What is the most predominant greenhouse gas?

    a. methane

    b. nitrous oxide

    c. carbon dioxide

    d. ground-level ozone

15. What causes a fatal lung disease called mesothelioma?

    a. asbestos

    b. ozone

    c. radon

    d. formaldehyde

Practice Test 2

1. What air pollutant originates primarily from motor vehicle emissions?

   a. particulates

   b. nitrogen dioxide

   c. sulfur dioxide

   d. carbon monoxide

2. A recent study found a correlation between Dieldrin, a popular pesticide used until the 1970s, and:

   a. lung cancer.

   b. breast cancer.

   c. ovarian cancer.

   d. prostate cancer.

3. Chemicals that contribute to the depletion of the ozone layer are called:

   a. ozone.

   b. chlorofluorocarbons.

   c. hydrocarbons.

   d. carbon monoxide.

4. Carbon dioxide, CFCs, ground-level ozone, nitrous oxide, and methane are types of:

   a. acid rain.

   b. greenhouse gases.

   c. chlorofluorocarbons.

   d. nonpoint source pollutants.

5. What is a major source of point source pollutants?

   a. construction wastes

   b. soil erosion and sedimentation

   c. pesticide and fertilizer runoff

   d. sewage treatment plants

6. Solid waste that poses a health hazard to humans or to the environment due to its toxic properties is called:

   a. municipal waste.

   b. environmental waste.

   c. hazardous waste.

   d. toxic waste.

7. What is the most dangerous type of radiation?

   a. kappa rays

   b. gamma rays

   c. beta particles

   d. alpha particles

8. A temperature inversion occurs when:

   a. a warm layer of air is trapped under a layer of cold air.

   b. a cool layer of air is trapped under a layer of warm air.

   c. the temperature drops more than 25 degrees in less than one hour.

   d. the temperature fluctuates within a 20-degree range in a 24-hour period.

9. Dan is concerned because insulation he used in the 1950s contained tiny fibers that can become loosened and airborne and embed themselves in the lungs. This type of insulation contained:

   a. lead.

   b. radon.

   c. asbestos.

   d. formaldehyde.

10. Strong-smelling gas, present in some carpets and adhesives, that can lead to central nervous system disorders and cancer, is called:

    a. radon.

    b. asbestos.

    c. ozone.

    d. formaldehyde.

11. Soon after Sandra and Dean moved into their new house, they began experiencing respiratory problems, dizziness, fatigue, nausea, and rashes. One possible source of their problem is a colorless, strong-smelling gas present in some carpets called:

    a. lead.

    b. asbestos.

    c. radon.

    d. formaldehyde.

12. Betsy lives in an older home that has cracks in the floor of the basement and foundation as well as an inadequately vented basement and attic. Betsy should buy a home-testing kit to check for:

    a. lead.

    b. radon.

    c. asbestos.

    d. formaldehyde.

13. Ed's job involves using herbicides. Ed is now experiencing nausea, vomiting, diarrhea, and painful sores. Ed may be suffering from the long-term effects of accumulating toxic substances in the herbicides called:

    a. THMs.

    b. PCPs.

    c. dioxins.

    d. leachates.

14. Superfund is associated with

    a. hazardous waste.

    b. global warming.

    c. air pollution.

    d. population control.

15. Nuclear power plants account for what percent of the total radiation to which we are exposed?

    a. less than 1 percent

    b. 10 percent

    c. 25 percent

    d. 50 percent

17
Consumerism

Chapter Overview

Today, consumers of health care services and products face many choices and challenges. Some fall prey to marketing and advertising campaigns that encourage the use of unnecessary products. Some individuals believe products work when, in actuality, they would have recovered without the use of the product. Other products appear to work simply because the consumer believes they work. Being an informed consumer will help you obtain optimal health care at an affordable cost.

A recent concept in health consumerism proposes that the patient is the primary health care provider. We can practice behaviors that promote health, prevent disease, and minimize the need to seek formal medical treatment. Self-care consists of knowing your body, paying attention to its signals, and taking appropriate action to stop the progression of illness or injury. Effective self-care also means understanding when to seek medical attention rather than treating a condition yourself.

Suppose you decide that you do need medical help. You must then identify what type of help you need and where to obtain it. Traditional Western allopathic medicine includes general practitioners and specialists, osteopaths, ophthalmologists, optometrists, dentists, and nurse practitioners. There are numerous types of medical practice configurations, such as sole practitioners, group practice, nonprofit (voluntary) hospitals run by religious or humanitarian groups, for-profit (nongovernmental) hospitals, and outpatient (ambulatory) care hospital clinics.

Cost, quality of care, and access to services are all important health care issues.

Health insurance providers can assist with medical expenses, but not everyone has health insurance. Private health insurance is costly. Social programs for those who do not have insurance include Medicare (for those over age 65) and Medicaid (for those defined as poor). Diagnosis related groups (DRGs) and managed care, health maintenance organizations (HMOs), and preferred provider organizations (PPOs) are programs that are attempting to control health care costs.

TAKE CHARGE WORKSHEET 17.1

Purchasing Appropriate Medical Supplies

DIRECTIONS: Check your home to see if you have the following items. It is a good idea to keep these items in one storage place for ease of access in an emergency situation.

_____ thermometer

_____ probe or thermometer covers

_____ tweezers

_____ pain relievers (acetaminophen, aspirin, ibuprofen, naproxen sodium)

_____ burn spray or water-based salve

_____ Calamine® lotion, Caladryl®, or an anti-puritic cream (for itching)

_____ Neosporin®, Bacitracin®, or other antiseptic ointment

_____ 4 x 4 dressings

_____ paper or adhesive tape

_____ scissors

_____ adhesive bandages

_____ disposable one-time use ice pack

_____ insurance information

_____ allergy, medication, and other emergency information

_____ emergency contact numbers (physician, parents, siblings, etc.)

Which Pain Reliever Is Which?

DIRECTIONS: Place the correct answer in the space provided to the left of the item.

_____ 1. This ingredient is in Tylenol® products.

     a. acetaminophen

     b. aspirin

     c. ibuprofen

     d. naproxen sodium

_____ 2. This product should not be given to children or someone with asthma or ulcers.

     a. acetaminophen

     b. aspirin

     c. ibuprofen

     d. naproxen sodium

_____ 3. This product acts by blocking pain receptors in the nervous system.

     a. acetaminophen

     b. aspirin

     c. ibuprofen

     d. naproxen sodium

_____ 4. This product relieves muscle soreness and pain, but is also good for headaches and fever.

     a. acetaminophen

     b. aspirin

     c. ibuprofen

     d. naproxen sodium

_____ 5. All of the above mentioned pain-reliever products can be used to reduce a fever.

     a. true

     b. false

NAME: _____ DATE: _____

TAKE CHARGE WORKSHEET 17.2

Advertisement Claims for Health Care Products:
A Cure, The Placebo Effect, or Spontaneous Remission?

DIRECTIONS: Numerous advertisers of health care products and services use attractive tactics to make the sale. Advertising claims sometimes appear to be supported by spontaneous remission or the placebo effect, rather than by the efficacy of the product or service. Go through magazines to find questionable advertisements of health care products and services. Cut out examples of products or services that claim to cure, but have not been proven to have a real effect.

For Further Thought

Visit the following website to learn about health care products and services that have not been proven to cure but claim to do so anyway:

http://www.quackwatch.org/
Quackwatch Home Page

NAME: _____ DATE: _____

TAKE CHARGE WORKSHEET 17.3

Finding Credible Information on the Web

DIRECTIONS: Review the list of websites below. Choose three websites from the list that interest you and for which you will write an evaluation.

List of Health-Related Websites

Databases for Searches

http://www.findarticles.com

http://www.medscape.com

http://www.healthfinder.gov

Mental Health Information

National Mental Health Association http://www.nmha.org

Stress Management Education http://www.unl.edu/stress/mgmt/

Sexuality Information

AIDS and HIV Information http://www.thebody.com/index.shtml

Columbia University's Health Question and Answer Internet Service
     http://www.goaskalice.columbia.edu/

Managing Contraception www.managingcontraception.com

The Sexuality Information and Education Council of the United States (SIECUS)
     http://www.siecus.org

Nutrition and Weight Control Information

American Dietetic Association http://www.eatright.org/

National Association of Anorexia Nervosa and Associated Disorders http://www.anad.org/

Overeaters Anonymous Headquarters http://www.overeatersanonymous.org/

Exercise and Fitness Information

American Heart Association http://www.justmove.org

Physical Activity and Health http://www.cdc.gov/nccdphp/sgr/sgr.htm

The President's Council on Physical Fitness and Sports http://www.fitness.gov

Disease Information

American Academy of Allergy, Asthma, and Immunology http://www.aaaai.org/

American Cancer Society http://www.cancer.org

American Heart Association http://americanheart.org

American Lung Association http://lungusa.org

NIH National Resource Center—Osteoporosis http://www.osteo.org/

National High Blood Pressure Education Program Center http://www.nhlbi.nih.gov

National Institute of Allergy and Infectious Disease http://www.niaid.nih.gov

National Osteoporosis Foundation http://www.nof.org/

Oncolink University of Pennsylvania Cancer Center http://www.oncolink.upenn.edu/

Drug and Alcohol Information

Marijuana Anonymous http://www.marijuana-anonymous.org/

National Council on Alcoholism and Drug Dependence http://www.ncadd.org

National Clearinghouse for Alcoholism and Drug Information http://www.health.org

National Collegiate Athletics Association Resource Exchange Center
http://www.drugfreesport.com/

National Institute on Alcohol Abuse and Alcoholism http://www.niaaa.nih.gov/

National Institute on Drug Abuse http://www.clubdrubs.org/

Quit Smoking Network http://www.quitnet.com

Quit Smoking Cigarettes http://www.megalink.net/ ~ dale/quitcigs.html

The Internet Drug List http://www.rxlist.com

Consumerism

Food and Drug Administration http://www.fda.gov

National Committee for Quality Assurance http://www.ncqa.org

Environmental Health

National Institute for Occupational Safety and Health http://www.cdc.gov/niosh/homepage.html

National Safety Council Environmental Health Center http://www.nsc.org/ehc.htm

The Internet Consumer Recycling Guide http://www.obviously.com/recycle/

Evaluation of Websites

DIRECTIONS: Write a one-page evaluation for each of the three websites you have chosen. Use the criteria below to guide your evaluation. At the beginning of your evaluation, include the name of the website, the URL of the website, and the date you visited the website.

Criteria for Evaluating a Website

Credibility of the Source. This includes who the authors are, where they received their information, whether the authors had any bias toward the subject, how current the information is, how relevant or useful the information is, and whether the material posted went through some type of editorial review process before it was published.

Content. This includes how accurate the information is, the evidence regarding accuracy, documentation regarding the source of information, any disclaimers about information provided, and important information that may have been omitted.

Disclosure. This includes the purpose of the site, whether the authors are asking users to give information, and whether that information could be used for hidden purposes.

Links. This includes the selection of links to other web pages, the design of the web page, descriptions of the links, and content of other links.

Design. This includes how accessible the web page is, whether it is logically organized or well put together, and if an internet search engine is provided to help find things easily.

Interactivity. This includes a feedback mechanism for readers, any chat rooms that are provided, and anything on the website that is tailored to the user.

Caveats. This includes any alerts which make the user aware of misleading claims.

NAME: _____ DATE: _____

TAKE CHARGE WORKSHEET 17.4

Stocking a First Aid Kit

DIRECTIONS: You may be required to give first aid to someone at your worksite, or you may want to have your own first aid kit available for emergency situations at home. Go to the local discount store or pharmacy and make sure you have the following items in order to stock your very own first aid kit.

The First Aid Container Must:

Be durable and have a secure latch.

Be large enough to contain all your supplies.

Be visibly marked with a large red cross for identification by others.

Have emergency numbers posted inside:

    Emergency Medical Services

    Poison Control

    Family physician

    Parents or other person to notify in the event of an emergency

Have the following personal information inside:

    Medical information

    Vaccination records

Contents of the First Aid Kit:

_____ 2 pairs of rubber gloves	_____ 2 splints
_____ pocket face mask	_____ towel or blanket
_____ adhesive bandages	_____ first aid reference book
_____ 2 x 3 gauze dressings (stored in plastic bag)	_____ Neosporin®/Bacitracin®
_____ 4 x 4 gauze dressings (stored in plastic bag)	_____ activated charcoal
_____ occlusive dressings (no adhesive, no air through)	_____ paper/pencil/pen
_____ extra plastic Ziploc® bags	_____ soap/water/saline solution
_____ adhesive or paper tape	_____ salt/sugar
_____ 2 inch roller gauze	_____ ice pack
_____ scissors	_____ thermometer
_____ Ace® wrap	_____ tweezers
_____ 2 triangular bandages	_____ small flashlight
_____ safety pins	

List additional items that you may want to include on the back of this worksheet.

General Review Questions

1. Explain the concept of self-care and provide examples.

2. What are three types of managed care plans?

3. Describe two major types of medical practices.

4. Distinguish between Medicare and Medicaid.

5. Discuss the essential elements of a managed care system.

Practice Test 1

1. Paul's headache disappeared after a week without receiving any treatment. This is an example of:
   a. disease prevention.
   b. the placebo effect.
   c. spontaneous remission.
   d. complementary medical treatment.

2. A medical practitioner who treats routine ailments, advises on preventive care, gives general medical advice, and makes appropriate referrals when necessary is called a:
   a. general practitioner.
   b. family primary provider.
   c. primary care practitioner.
   d. primary family physician.

3. A midlevel practitioner trained to handle most standard cases of care is called a:
   a. physician's assistant.
   b. nurse practitioner.
   c. licensed practical nurse.
   d. physician's technician.

4. Jeff has received training similar to a medical doctor's but puts special emphasis on the skeletal and muscular systems. Jeff is a(n):
   a. internist.
   b. osteopath.
   c. general practitioner.
   d. endocrinologist.

5. What is the term used to refer to a private (for-profit) hospital that transfers a patient to a public hospital due to inability to pay?

    a. skimming

    b. patient dumping

    c. GOMERS

    d. bumping

6. Hospitals run by religious or other humanitarian groups that reinvest their earnings in the hospital to improve health care are called:

    a. nonprofit hospitals.

    b. for-profit hospitals.

    c. outpatient care centers.

    d. health maintenance organizations.

7. George has a suspicious growth on his back that his doctor wants to have biopsied. What type of ambulatory facility will he most likely go to for his biopsy?

    a. hospital

    b. surgicenter

    c. emergency center

    d. cancer treatment center

8. If you have glaucoma, you need to see a(n):

    a. osteopath.

    b. optometrist.

    c. hematologist.

    d. ophthamologist.

9. The common cold will improve with time, with or without treatment. This concept relates to

    a. the placebo effect.

    b. spontaneous remission.

    c. the holistic approach.

    d. complementary and alternative medicine.

10. Deb, age 23, is on welfare. Her medical bills are paid by a federal-state health insurance program for the poor called:

    a. HMO.

    b. Social Security.

    c. Medicaid.

    d. Medicare.

11. A specialist who diagnoses and treats diseases of the teeth, gums, and oral cavity is a(n)

    a. dentist.

    b. orthodontist.

    c. oral surgeon.

    d. osteopath.

12. Which of the following is *not* an HMO system?

    a. staff model

    b. group network model

    c. independent practice association

    d. preferred provider organization

13. What type of hospitals have traditionally been run by religious or other humanitarian groups?

    a. nonprofit hospitals

    b. private hospitals

    c. for-profit hospitals

    d. specialty hospitals

14. Surgicenters provide for all of the following types of medical care, *except*:

    a. vasectomy.

    b. heart surgery.

    c. tissue biopsy.

    d. cosmetic surgery.

15. Cost-control procedures used by health insurers to coordinate treatment is called:

    a. health maintenance.

    b. managed care.

    c. coordinated care.

    d. prepaid health care.

Practice Test 2

1. What medical practice is based on scientifically validated methods and procedures whose objective is to heal by countering the patient's symptoms?

    a. allopathic medicine

    b. nonallopathic medicine

    c. osteopathic medicine

    d. chiropractic medicine

2. What percent of the population is believed to be exceptionally susceptible to the power of suggestion and may be easy targets for aggressive health marketing?

    a. 1 percent

    b. 10 percent

    c. 20 percent

    d. 33 percent

3. In 2000, what percent of all surgeries in the United States involved an overnight hospital stay?

    a. less than 30 percent

    b. 50 percent

    c. 68 percent

    d. more than 85 percent

4. What is the most restrictive type of managed care?

    a. fee-for-service

    b. health maintenance organizations

    c. point of service

    d. preferred provider organization

5. Medicaid is financed by:

    a. Social Security.

    b. the state government only.

    c. the federal government only.

    d. both the state and federal government.

6. Tom is enrolled in an organized health care system that provides comprehensive services for a fixed, prepaid fee. What is this type of arrangement called?

    a. HMO

    b. DRG

    c. APPO

    d. PPA

7. Dorothy, age 71, has her medical bills paid by a federal health insurance program for the elderly and the permanently disabled. What is this program?

    a. HMO

    b. Social Security

    c. Medicaid

    d. Medicare

8. What effect is an apparent cure brought about by a substance that has no recognized therapeutic value?

    a. phantom

    b. placebo

    c. concurrent

    d. attribution

9. Jerry, age 67, was told in advance of her hospital stay that the hospital will be reimbursed by Medicare for only the first three days of her hospital visit due to a federal payment system that uses diagnostic categories called:

   a. PPOs.

   b. RBRVs.

   c. DRGs.

   d. HMOs.

10. Alice is enrolled in a health care plan that gives her a list of doctors. If she uses these doctors, she is reimbursed at a higher rate than if she chooses to go outside the plan. What is this type of arrangement called?

    a. HMO

    b. RBRV

    c. DRG

    d. PPO

11. The phenomenon of *job lock* led the federal government to pass legislation mandating

    a. diagnosis related groups.

    b. managed-care health plans.

    c. Medicare and Medicaid.

    d. the portability of health insurance benefits.

12. A federal health insurance program for the elderly and the permanently disabled is called

    a. Medicare.

    b. Medicaid.

    c. Title 19.

    d. managed care.

13. HMOs contract with providers to supply health services for enrollees through various systems. Under what system do you receive care from salaried staff doctors at the HMO's facility?

    a. staff model

    b. group network model

    c. independent practice association

    d. point of service

14. The type of medical practice in which a group of physicians combines resources and shares offices, equipment, and staff costs is called a:

    a. solo practice.

    b. group practice.

    c. fee-for-service practice.

    d. for-profit practice.

15. Under what type of managed care plan can patients go to providers outside their HMO for care, but they must pay for the extra cost?

    a. preferred provider

    b. point of service

    c. health maintenance organization

    d. independent practice association

18

Complementary and Alternative Medicine

Chapter Overview

Complementary and alternative medicine are terms used to describe techniques that are distinct from traditional, allopathic medicine, and until recently, were neither taught in U.S. medical schools nor available in U.S. hospitals. There is a wide variety of complementary health practices available today. Traditional oriental medicine emphasizes proper balance of the qi ("chi"), and treatments include acupuncture, herbal medicine, and massage. Ayurvedic medicine places equal emphasis on body, mind, and spirit to restore harmony to the individual. Ayurvedic treatments include massage, steam baths, exposure to sunlight, controlled breathing, dietary modifications, and herbal remedies. Homeopathy is based on the principle that very small doses of the same substance that—in large doses—makes you sick, will make you better. Homeopathic physicians use diluted forms of herbal medicines, chemicals, and minerals to ward off illness. Naturopathic medicine views the body as capable of healing itself. The exclusion of impurities and harmful substances from the environment and the body is a way to restore health, not necessarily cure disease. Naturopathic medicine employs such healing practices as diet, homeopathy, acupuncture, herbal medicine, hydrotherapy, spinal and soft-tissue manipulation, electrical currents, ultrasound, light therapy, counseling, and pharmacology.

Chiropractic medicine is based on the idea that life-giving energy flows through the spine and the misalignment of the spine blocks this energy, causing pain. Spinal manipulation is used to reduce pain and restore energy. Other body manipulation therapies include energy therapies such as qi gong, Reiki, and therapeutic touch, and acupuncture and acupressure.

Insurance companies may or may not cover expenses from alternative medical practitioners. Most alternative medicine practitioners are trained and licensed, including chiropractors, massage therapists, and herbalists. Training and the scope of practice varies, so it is a good idea to investigate before you see an alternative medicine practitioner. The number of alternative practitioners is increasing, creating a greater number of options for consumers. The Center for Complementary and Alternative Medicine, created by the U.S. government, explores the effectiveness of practices used by these practitioners.

Herbal remedies are becoming increasingly popular. Ginko biloba is used for depression, PMS, to improve circulation, and to aid short-term memory and concentration. St. John's Wort is used for depression, as a sleep aid, and as an immune system support. Echinacea is used to shorten the duration and decrease the intensity of a cold. Ginseng is used to increase energy. Glucosamine is used to provide relief for sore joints. While some of these may be helpful to some people, they are not effective for everyone and potential side-effects or drug interactions should be considered. Foods such as soy, garlic, green tea, ginger, and yogurt appear to have health-promoting qualities as well.

Testimonials and other claims used to sell products should be viewed with caution. A wise consumer should seek reliable and accurate information and avoid practitioners who claim their products and services will cure everything. The best type of medicine is preventive medicine: exercising, eating well, and managing other aspects of life to maintain optimal health.

NAME: _____ DATE: _____

TAKE CHARGE WORKSHEET 18.1

Researching Complementary and Alternative Medicine

DIRECTIONS: Research websites to learn more about complementary and alternative medicine. Answer the following questions for an in-depth study of CAM.

1. Identify one CAM therapy in which you are interested, such as biologically based therapies, and study examples of that therapy (such as dietary supplements and herbal products).

2. Find examples of alternative medical systems that have developed in Western cultures as well as those that have developed in non-Western cultures.

3. There are five major types of complementary and alternative medicines. What type of CAM therapy appeals to you and why?

4. What is integrative medicine?

5. Identify a disease of interest. Learn how CAM therapies have been used to treat the given disease.

Websites

http://nccam.nih.gov/health/
National Center for Complementary and Alternative Medicine

http://www.rosenthal.hs.columbia.edu/
The Richard and Hinda Rosenthal Center for Complementary and Alternative Medicine

http://www.athealth.com/Practitioner/Newsletter/FPN_3_40.html
Alternative Medicine

http://www.altmedicine.com/
Alternative Health News Online

NAME: _____ DATE: _____

TAKE CHARGE WORKSHEET 18.2

Health Practitioners

DIRECTIONS: Draw a line from the type of degree in the left column to its definition in the right column to test your knowledge of the variant types of health practitioners available to you as a consumer.

_____ 1. R. N.

_____ 2. R. N. A.

_____ 3. F. N. P

_____ 4. R. N.–C.

_____ 5. P. A.–C.

_____ 6. N. P.

_____ 7. D. O.

_____ 8. O. D.

_____ 9. M. D.

_____ 10. D. P. M.

_____ 11. D. M. D.

_____ 12. D. D. S.

_____ 13. D. V. M.

_____ 14. G. P.

_____ 15. Board Certified

_____ 16. F. A. A. P.

_____ 17. F. A. C. S.

_____ 18. F. A. A. C. P.

_____ 19. F. A. C. A. A. I.

_____ 20. F. A. C. O. G.

a. Fellow of the American Academy of Chest Physicians

b. Registered Nurse Board Certified

c. Physician's Assistant Board Certified

d. Family Nurse Practitioner

e. Medical Doctor

f. Fellow of the American College of Obstetrics and Gynecology

g. Fellow of the American College of Allergy, Asthma, and Immunology

h. Registered Nurse

i. Doctor of Dentistry Specialization

j. Doctor of Veterinary Medicine

k. Doctor of Osteopathy

l. Fellow of the American Academy of Pediatrics

m. Doctor of Optometry

n. Doctor of Podiatric Medicine

o. Nurse Practitioner

p. Registered Nurse Anesthetist

q. Fellow of the American College of Surgeons

r. Passed the State or National Board Examinations for Specialty

s. General Practitioner

t. Doctorate of Medical Dentistry

Answers

1. h, 2. p, 3. d, 4. b, 5. c, 6. o, 7. k, 8. m, 9. e, 10. n, 11. t,
12. i, 13. j, 14. s, 15. r, 16. l, 17. q, 18. a, 19. g, 20. f.

TAKE CHARGE WORKSHEET 18.3

Risky Business: Let the Buyer Beware

DIRECTIONS: Answer the following questions after you have read Chapter 18, taken the time to form opinions regarding complementary and alternative medicine, and done research on the Internet.

1. If a person's eczema went away after one reflexology treatment, would you say the reflexologist cured the eczema? Why or why not?

2. If a nutritionist told you that lecithin capsules improved your memory, would you take it? Why or why not?

3. What types of credentials would you look for when someone said they were an herbalist?

4. If a magazine advertised a new product that will help you lose weight and have more energy, what other sources would you consult before purchasing the product?

5. If a friend sounded very convincing about a new business involving the sale of a very new health product, would you be interested? Why or why not?

6. Define *placebo effect*.

7. If a physician advertised their services and used testimonials of former patients regarding the effectiveness of their new treatment, would you consider going to that physician?

8. How would you know for certain whether an on-line webpage with medical advice was legitimate?

9. Do you think it is necessary for a substance to have undergone controlled studies before it is recommended for use?

10. If a physician recommends surgery, what types of questions should you ask?

11. Do you have a right to ask questions about how much a procedure will cost before granting permission to proceed?

12. What clues would you look for in an advertisement that might be giving false information?

13. What sorts of things would you look for on the label of an herbal supplement before purchasing the product?

14. Would you consider purchasing protein powder in a gallon-sized jug if the salesperson told you that that was the only size it came in and that it cost $50.00?

15. Do you ask for generic prescription substitutes if a doctor prescribes a brand name?

16. Do you compare at least three different health-related products before purchasing them? If you did this, what would you learn?

17. Have you ever investigated what the Consumer Product Safety Commission, Food and Drug Administration, and other agencies do to protect consumers? What did you find in your research?

General Review Questions

1. Distinguish between complementary and alternative medicine.

2. Describe homeopathy and naturopathy.

3. Discuss the alternative medical systems that are based on manipulation and/or movement of the body.

4. Name three types of energy therapies.

5. How can you protect yourself when using alternative treatments?

Practice Test 1

1. What is the most frequently used alternative to conventional medicine?

   a. massage
   b. energy healing
   c. chiropractic
   d. relaxation techniques

2. What alternative system of medicine places equal emphasis on body, mind, and spirit and strives to restore the innate harmony of the individual?

   a. Ayurvedic medicine
   b. homeopathic medicine
   c. naturopathic medicine
   d. traditional oriental medicine

3. Massage, steam baths, exposure to sunlight, and controlled breathing are among some of the more common forms of:

   a. traditional oriental treatments.

   b. naturopathic treatments.

   c. Ayurveda treatments.

   d. homeopathic treatments.

4. What alternative system of medicine is based on the principle that "like cures like"?

   a. naturopathic medicine

   b. homeopathic medicine

   c. Ayurvedic medicine

   d. traditional oriental medicine

5. What alternative system of medicine emphasizes restoring health rather than curing disease?

   a. homeopathic medicine

   b. naturopathic medicine

   c. Ayurvedic medicine

   d. chiropractic medicine

6. All of the following are energy therapies, *except*:

   a. qi gong.

   b. Reiki.

   c. therapeutic touch.

   d. naturopathy.

7. A component of traditional Chinese medicine that combines movement, meditation, and regulation of breathing to enhance the flow of vital energy, improve blood circulation, and enhance immune function is called:

   a. Reiki.

   b. tai chi.

   c. qi gong.

   d. shiatsu.

8. What method is based on the belief that by channeling spiritual energy through the practitioner, the spirit is healed, and it in turn heals the physical body?

   a. Reiki

   b. qi gong

   c. tai chi

   d. shiatsu

9. Functional foods are also known as:

   a. phytomedicines.

   b. antioxidants.

   c. ergogenic aids.

   d. nutraceuticals.

10. Which healthful food can lower "bad" LDL cholesterol?

    a. soy protein

    b. ginger

    c. yogurt

    d. oat fiber

11. A popular complementary treatment that uses scented materials to evoke sensations through the smell centers of the body is called:

    a. energy healing.

    b. hypnosis.

    c. iridology.

    d. aromatherapy.

12. What type of medicine is based on the idea that a life-giving energy flows through the spine via the nervous sytem?

    a. homeopathic medicine

    b. naturopathic medicine

    c. chiropractic medicine

    d. Ayurvedic medicine

13. Which of the following complementary treatments is based on the philosophy that humans produce waves of energy that are disrupted during illness?

a. energy healing

b. massage

c. iridology

d. aromatherapy

14. The German Commission E attempts to:

a. regulate CAM practitioners.

b. educate the public about CAM.

c. regulate sales of alternative medicines and supplements.

d. study side effects of CAM.

15. What energy therapy is derived from the ancient technique of "laying on" of hands?

a. Reiki

b. qi gong

c. therapeutic touch

d. acupressure

Practice Test 2

1. What practitioner diagnoses mostly by observation and touch and assigns patients to one of three body types?

a. chiropractic practitioner

b. naturopathic practitioner

c. Ayurvedic practitioner

d. homeopathic practitioner

2. The Ayurvedic system is based on what country's traditional system of medicine?

a. China

b. India

c. Japan

d. Mexico

3. What form of body work aims to restructure the musculoskeletal system by working on patterns of tension held in deep tissue?

a. rolfing

b. shiatsu

c. Trager work

d. qi gong

4. What substance has been shown to be effective for treating osteoarthritis and related degenerative joint diseases?

a. ginseng

b. creatine

c. echinacea

d. glucosamine

5. What food fights motion sickness, stomach pain, and upset, and discourages blood clots?

a. garlic

b. ginger

c. sunflower

d. oat fiber

6. Beta-carotene, selenium, vitamin C, and vitamin E are the primary

a. antioxidants.

b. muscle enhancers.

c. glucosamines.

d. nutraceuticals.

7. Two purported remedies for depression are:

    a. gingko biloba and St. John's wort.

    b. gingko biloba and echinacea.

    c. St. John's wort and Kava.

    d. St. John's wort and echinacea.

8. Gingko biloba is used to treat:

    a. constipation.

    b. memory loss.

    c. premenstrual syndrome.

    d. sleep disturbances.

9. Medical alternatives to traditional medicine are known as:

    a. allopathic medicine.

    b. primary medicine.

    c. nonallopathic medicine.

    d. chiropractic medicine.

10. The Chinese art of inserting fine needles at various points of the skin that fall along pathways of energy is known as:

    a. iridology.

    b. reflexology.

    c. acupuncture.

    d. acupressure

11. Which of the following treatments is based on the idea that a life-giving energy flows through the spine and if the spine is sub-laxated, that life force is disrupted?

    a. podiatric

    b. orthopedic

    c. osteopathic

    d. chiropractic

12. Naturopaths believe that illness results when:

    a. large doses of drugs are taken by a person.

    b. the spine is partially dislocated and the life force is disrupted.

    c. natural principles relating to lifestyle and environment have been violated.

    d. the nervous system is distressed.

13. A nonallopathic practice that is based on the medicinal qualities of plants or herbs is called:

    a. osteopathic medicine.

    b. homeopathic medicine.

    c. naturopathic medicine.

    d. chiropractic medicine.

14. What Chinese medical treatment has been shown to improve quality of life and improve or cure certain health conditions?

    a. massage

    b. acupressure

    c. homeopathy

    d. herbal medicine

15. What element of traditional oriental medicine refers to the vital energy force that courses through the body?

    a. qi

    b. Reiki

    c. tai chi

    d. shiatsu

Appendix
Answers

Chapter 1

General Review Questions

1. Mortality is the death rate; morbidity is the illness rate. p. 4

2. Other factors influencing your health status include interpersonal, social, and work influences; community influences; heredity, access to health care, and the environment. p. 16

3. Vaccinations, motor vehicle safety, workplace safety, control of infectious diseases, reduction of cardiovascular disease, food safety, maternal and infant care, family planning, fluoridation, anti-smoking campaigns. p. 13

4. Many people are highly influenced by the approval or disapproval of significant others. Such influences can support healthy behavior, or they can interfere with even the best intentions. p. 20

5. Shaping involves using a series of small steps to get to a particular goal gradually. Visualization involves practicing through mental rehearsal. Modeling involves learning behaviors through close observation of other people. Controlling the situation involves choosing the right setting or right group of people to positively influence behaviors. Reinforcement involves using rewards to increase the likelihood that a behavior change will occur. Changing self-talk involves changing the way you think and talk to yourself. p. 21

Practice Test 1

1. B, p. 3	6. A, p. 18	11. A, p. 13
2. B, p. 4	7. C, p. 13	12. B, p. 19
3. A, p. 4	8. D, p. 13	13. A, p. 21
4. D, p. 4	9. A, p. 18	14. A, p. 22
5. D, p. 20	10. C, p. 13	15. D, p. 10

Practice Test 2

1. B, p. 13	6. C, p. 4	11. A, p. 20
2. B, p. 15	7. A, p. 13	12. B, p. 18
3. B, p. 4	8. B, p. 18	13. D, p. 21
4. B, p. 13	9. A, p. 22	14. C, p. 23
5. B, p. 11	10. B, p. 5	15. C, p. 21

Chapter 2

General Review Questions

1. Psychosocial health encompasses the mental, emotional, social, and spiritual dimensions of health. p. 30

2. Psychosocially healthy people feel good about themselves, feel comfortable with other people, control tension and anxiety, are able to meet the demands of life, curb hate and guilt, maintain a positive outlook, enrich the lives of others, cherish the things that make them smile, value diversity, and appreciate and respect nature. pp. 31–32

3. There are four basic types of emotions: emotions resulting from harm, loss, or threats; emotions resulting from benefits; borderline emotions, such as hope and compassion; and more complex emotions, such as grief, disappointment, bewilderment, and curiosity. p. 32

4. The four major themes of spirituality are interconnectedness, practice of mindfulness, spirituality as part of daily life, and living in harmony with our community. pp. 35–36

5. Anxiety disorders include generalized anxiety disorder, panic disorder, specific phobias, and social phobias. p. 46

Practice Test 1

1. A, p. 33	6. A, p. 38	11. C, p. 45
2. B, p. 32	7. B, p. 47	12. B, p. 43
3. C, p. 36	8. B, p. 39	13. A, p. 49
4. D, p. 40	9. B, p. 38	14. B, p. 52
5. B, p. 30	10. B, p. 44	15. C, p. 48

Practice Test 2

1. D, p. 36	6. A, p. 38	11. D, p. 51
2. C, p. 42	7. D, p. 47	12. B, p. 47
3. B, p. 36	8. C, p. 47	13. D, p. 50
4. B, p. 46	9. A, p. 41	14. D, p. 40
5. A, p. 38	10. B, p. 44	15. D, p. 49

Chapter 3

General Review Questions

1. Psychosocial stressors include change, hassles, pressure, inconsistent goals and behaviors, conflict, overload, burnout, and discrimination. p. 62

2. The three phases of the GAS are alarm, resistance, and exhaustion. p. 57

3. Undue stress for extended periods of time can compromise the immune system and result in serious health consequences. Stress has been linked to numerous health problems, including CVD, cancer, and increased susceptibility to infectious diseases. pp. 59–61

4. Fight technostress through exercise, becoming aware of what you are doing, setting up strict rules for when you can long on, giving yourself more time for everything you do, managing the phone, setting "time out" periods, taking regular breaks, stretching, resisting the urge to buy the latest technological gadget, leaving technology behind when on vacation, and backing up materials on your computer at regular intervals. p. 60

5. Exercise reduces stress by raising levels of endorphins in the bloodstream. Exercise increases energy, reduces hostility, and improves mental alertness. It also can be a source of social interaction, which further reduces stressor effects. p. 73

Practice Test 1

1. B, p. 56	6. D, p. 59	11. A, p. 57
2. B, p. 59	7. D, p. 63	12. C, p. 67
3. C, p. 58	8. B, p. 57	13. C, p. 67
4. B, p. 57	9. A, p. 58	14. D, p. 70
5. B, p. 58	10. D, p. 69	15. C, p. 61

Practice Test 2

1. A, p. 57	6. D, p. 63	11. B, p. 75
2. C, p. 57	7. C, p. 57	12. C, p. 59
3. C, p. 57	8. B, p. 57	13. D, p. 69
4. B, p. 59	9. D, p. 59	14. B, p. 76
5. C, p. 57	10. A, p. 58	15. C, p. 58

Chapter 4

General Review Questions

1. Commonly listed causes include poverty, unemployment, parental influence, cultural beliefs, the media, discrimination, oppression, religious differences, breakdowns in the criminal justice system, and stress. pp. 83–84

2. Anger is a predictor of future aggressive behavior. Substance abuse also appears to be a form of "ignition" for violence. p. 84

3. There are many reasons why some women find it difficult to break their ties with their abusers. Some women are financially dependent on their partners. Others fear retaliation. Some hope that the situation will change over time. Some stay because their cultural or religious beliefs forbid divorce. Some still love the abusive partner. Some can get caught in a cycle of tension building, acute battering, and remorse/reconciliation. pp. 91–92

4. Social contributors to sexual assault include minimization, trivialization, blaming the victim, and the assumption that "boys will be boys." p. 97

5. Community strategies for prevention must be multidimensional. An example of a successful strategy is developing and implementing educational programs to teach communication, conflict resolution, and coping skills. p. 100

Practice Test 1

1. A, p. 84	6. A, p. 87	11. A, p. 95
2. D, p. 94	7. D, p. 92	12. C, p. 97
3. B, p. 89	8. A, p. 92	13. C, p. 90
4. A, p.94	9. C, p. 92	14. D, p. 91
5. B, p. 92	10. B, p. 95	15. C, p. 82

Practice Test 2

1. D, p. 84	6. C, p. 97	11. D, p. 91
2. A, p. 86	7. C, p. 97	12. C, p. 95
3. C, p. 95	8. A, p. 97	13. A, p. 92
4. D, p. 95	9. A, p. 95	14. B, p. 92
5. A, p. 89	10. C, p. 94	15. B, p. 102

Chapter 5

General Review Questions

1. Learning to self-disclose and learning to listen. p. 106

2. Barriers to intimacy include lack of personal identity, emotional immaturity, and a poorly developed sense of responsibility. p. 113

3. Causes of jealousy typically include: overdependence on the relationship; high value on sexual exclusivity; severity of the threat; low self-esteem; and fear of losing control. p. 115

4. Excitement/arousal, plateau, orgasm, and resolution. p. 129

5. Today's family structure looks different from that of previous generations, but love, trust, and commitment to a child's welfare continue to be the cornerstone of successful childrearing. p. 119

Practice Test 1

1. B, p. 108	6. D, p. 116	11. D, p. 126
2. C, p. 110	7. D, p. 109	12. D, p. 127
3. A, p. 109	8. B, p. 120	13. C, p. 130
4. B, p. 116	9. D, p. 123	14. A, p. 129
5. D, p. 108	10. B, p. 126	15. B, p. 133

Practice Test 2

1. B, p. 108	6. A, p. 116	11. A, p. 133
2. C, p. 110	7. D, p. 118	12. B, p. 133
3. A, p. 113	8. B, p. 121	13. A, p. 124
4. B, p. 111	9. C, p. 115	14. B, p. 122
5. D, p. 113	10. C, p. 127	15. C, p. 125

Chapter 6

General Review Questions

1. A viable egg, a viable sperm, and access to the egg by the sperm are the necessary conditions. p. 140

2. They rely upon the alteration of sexual behavior. p. 150

3. Perfect failure rate refers to the number of pregnancies that are likely to occur in a year if the method is used absolutely perfectly, that is, without any error. The typical use failure rate refers to the number of pregnancies that are likely to occur with typical use, that is, with the normal number of errors, memory lapses, and incorrect or incomplete use. p. 140

4. Types of fertility awareness methods include the cervical mucus method, the body temperature method, and the calendar method. p. 150

5. Emotional health, maternal health, paternal health, financial status, and contingency planning. p. 154

Practice Test 1

1. C, p. 142	6. A, p. 162	11. B, p. 148
2. D, p. 150	7. B, p. 161	12. D, p. 144
3. A, p. 169	8. C, p. 164	13. B, p. 150
4. A, p. 158	9. D, p. 142	14. B, p. 166
5. B, p. 157	10. C, p. 163	15. B, p. 167

Practice Test 2

1. B, p. 157	6. C, p. 164	11. C, p. 146
2. C, p. 158	7. C, p. 164	12. A, p. 167
3. C, p. 164	8. B, p. 161	13. A, p. 166
4. A, p. 148	9. B, p. 152	14. B, p. 158
5. D, p. 145	10. B, p. 145	15. C, p. 160

Chapter 7

General Review Questions

1. a) Prescription drugs can be obtained only with the written prescription of a licensed physician; b) over-the-counter drugs can be purchased in supermarkets without a prescription; c) recreational drugs are legal drugs that help people relax and socialize; d) herbal preparations are substances of plant origin that may have medicinal properties; e) illicit drugs are illegal and psychoactive, and are generally recognized as harmful; f) commercial preparations are commonly used chemical substances including cosmetics and household cleaning products. pp. 173–174

2. Oral ingestion, injection, inhalation, inunction, suppositories. p. 174

3. All addictions are characterized by four symptoms: compulsion, loss of control, negative consequences, and denial. p. 176

4. The Food and Drug Administration regularly reviews prescription drugs to evaluate if they would be suitable as OTC drugs. To change to OTC status, the following criteria must be met: 1) The drug has been marketed as a prescription drug for at least three years. 2) The use of the drug has been relatively high since becoming available as a prescription drug. 3) Adverse drug reactions are not alarming. p. 178

5. Drugs are classified into five schedules based on their potential for abuse, their medical uses, and accepted standards of safe use. p. 183

Practice Test 1

1. D, p. 176
2. B, p. 174
3. B, p. 174
4. D, p. 174
5. C, p. 176

6. A, p. 188
7. C, p. 176
8. A, p. 176
9. B, p. 180
10. A, p. 185

11. D, pp. 186–187
12. B, p. 184
13. D, p. 193
14. B, p. 193
15. B, p. 183

Practice Test 2

1. B, p. 175
2. A, p. 174
3. D, p. 186
4. C, p. 180
5. C, p. 180

6. D, p. 180
7. A, p. 178
8. C, p. 179
9. B, p. 180
10. D, p. 183

11. A, p. 183
12. B, p. 174
13. A, p. 192
14. B, p. 180
15. B, p. 174

Chapter 8

General Review Questions

1. Several factors influence how quickly your body absorbs alcohol: the alcohol concentration in your drink, the amount of alcohol you consume, the amount of food in your stomach, pylorospasm, and your mood. p. 204

2. Long-term effects include diseases of the nervous system, cardiovascular system, and liver, and some cancers. pp. 206–207

3. FAS effects are mental retardation; small head; tremors; and abnormalities of the face, limbs, heart, and brain. p. 207

4. Cancer, cardiovascular disease, respiratory disorders, and impotence. pp. 218–221

5. Because caffeine meets the requirements for addiction—tolerance, psychological dependence, and withdrawal symptoms—it can be classified as addictive. p. 226

Practice Test 1

1. B, p. 204	6. C, p. 212	11. B, p. 221
2. B, p. 201	7. A, p. 207	12. D, p. 213
3. A, p. 204	8. A, p. 218	13. C, p. 225
4. C, p. 205	9. A, p. 218	14. A, p. 209
5. B, p. 211	10. A, p. 224	15. D, p. 224

Practice Test 2

1. B, p. 211	6. C, p. 211	11. A, p. 224
2. B, p. 212	7. C, p. 207	12. D, p. 209
3. D, p. 203	8. A, p. 219	13. D, p. 226
4. A, p. 215	9. D, p. 216	14. A, p. 209
5. A, p. 225	10. C, p. 218	15. A, p. 224

Chapter 9

General Review Questions

1. Powerful influences include: personal preferences, habit, ethnic heritage or tradition, social interactions, availability, emotional comfort, values, body image, and nutrition. pp. 232–233

2. Breads, ceral, rice and pasta group (6–11 servings); vegetable group (3–5 servings); fruit group (2–4 servings); milk, yogurt, and cheese group (2–3 servings); and meat, poultry, fish, dry beans, eggs, and nuts group (2–3 servings). p. 234

3. The benefits of fiber include: protection against colon and rectal cancer, breast cancer, constipation, diverticulosis, heart disease, diabetes, and obesity. pp. 242–243

4. Whereas LDLs transport cholesterol to the body's cells, HDLs apparently transport circulating cholesterol to the liver for metabolism and elimination from the body. p. 244

5. Women have a lower ratio of lean body mass to adipose tissue at all ages and stages of life. Also, after sexual maturation, the rate of metabolism is higher in men, which means that they will burn more calories doing the same activities. p. 256

Practice Test 1

1. A, p. 233	6. B, p. 243	11. A, p. 237
2. A, p. 238	7. C, p. 244	12. B, p. 241
3. C, p. 240	8. B, p. 238	13. B, p. 249
4. D, p. 241	9. A, p. 234	14. A, p. 243
5. C, p. 240	10. C, p. 249	15. D, p. 249

Practice Test 2

1. D, p. 258	6. A, p. 244	11. B, p. 242
2. B, p. 240	7. B, p. 246	12. A, p. 238
3. B, p. 249	8. C, p. 264	13. D, p. 240
4. C, p. 242	9. A, p. 241	14. A, p. 243
5. B, p. 243	10. C, p. 238	15. A, p. 249

Chapter 10

General Review Questions

1. Overweight refers to increased body weight in relation to height, when compared to a standard, such as height and weight charts. Obesity is defined as an excessively high amount of body fat or adipose tissue in relation to lean body mass. More than 64.5 percent of Americans are overweight or obese. pp. 268–270

2. Hydrostatic weighing techniques; pinch and skinfold measures; girth and circumference measures; soft-tissue roentgenogram; bioelectrical impedance analysis; total body electrical conductivity. pp. 271–273

3. Healthy weights are defined as those associated with BMIs of 19 to 25. The desirable range for females falls between 21 and 23; for males, between 22 and 24. p. 271

4. A calorie is a unit of measure that indicates the amount of energy we obtain from a particular food. p. 283

5. Setpoint theory is a theory of obesity causation that suggests that fat storage is determined by a thermostatic mechanism in the body that acts to maintain a specific amount of body fat. p. 279

Practice Test 1

1. D, p. 270	6. B, p. 275	11. A, p. 281
2. B, p. 270	7. B, p. 270	12. A, p. 275
3. C, p. 273	8. A, p. 290	13. A, p. 271
4. B, p. 271	9. D, p. 286	14. D, p. 275
5. B, p. 270	10. C, p. 271	15. A, p. 275

Practice Test 2

1. B, p. 270	6. B, p. 280	11. A, p. 280
2. C, p. 271	7. C, p. 279	12. A, p. 283
3. B, p. 271	8. B, p. 291	13. B, p. 283
4. B, p. 274	9. C, p. 290	14. C, p. 291
5. D, p. 291	10. A, p. 283	15. A, p. 290

Chapter 11

General Review Questions

1. Improved cardiorespiratory fitness; improved bone mass; improved weight control; improved health and lifespan; improved mental health and stress management. p. 297

2. The major components of physical fitness include cardiorespiratory fitness, flexibility, muscular strength and endurance, and body composition. p. 296

3. Osteoporosis is more common among women than among men because women live longer than men, they have lower peak bone mass than men, and they lose bone mass at rates nearly twice as great as men after age 35. p. 298

4. Plantar fasciitis is an inflammation of the tissue on the bottom of the foot, usually caused by repetitive weight-bearing fitness activities such as running. Shin splints is the term used for any pain that occurs below the knee and above the ankle. It is frequently caused by running. Runner's knee describes a series of problems involving the muscles, tendons, and ligaments around the knee. The main symptom is pain experienced when downward pressure is applied to the kneecap after the knee is straightened fully. p. 310

5. Heat cramps are heat-related muscle cramps. Heat exhaustion is actually a mild form of shock caused by excessive water loss. Heat stroke is a life-threatening emergency condition which occurs when the body produces more heat than it has the capacity to deal with. p. 311

Practice Test 1

1. C, p. 298
2. B, p. 300
3. B, p. 298
4. A, p. 300
5. A, p. 300

6. C, p. 308
7. A, p. 302
8. D, p. 308
9. B, p. 303
10. C, p. 310

11. D, p. 306
12. C, p. 307
13. B, p. 311
14. C, p. 309
15. B, p. 311

Practice Test 2

1. B, p. 306
2. B, p. 301
3. C, p. 307
4. A, p. 309
5. C, p. 313

6. D, p. 297
7. B, p. 310
8. C, p. 313
9. A, p. 300
10. C, p. 301

11. B, p. 310
12. B, p. 311
13. A, p. 311
14. C, p. 297
15. C, p. 303

Chapter 12

General Review Questions

1. Atherosclerosis, coronary heart disease, chest pain, irregular heartbeat, congestive heart failure, congenital and rheumatic heart disease, and stroke. p. 322

2. Smoking, fatty diet, overweight, inactivity, high stress. p. 326

3. Deoxygenated blood enters the right atrium after having been circulated through the body. From the right atrium, blood moves to the right ventricle and is pumped through the pulmonary artery to the lungs, where it receives oxygen. Oxygenated blood from the lungs then returns to the left atrium of the heart. Blood from the left atrium is forced into the left ventricle. The left ventricle pumps blood through the aorta to all body parts. p. 319

4. An electrocardiogram is a record of the electrical activity of the heart. An angiography involves injecting dye into the heart and taking an x-ray to discover which areas are blocked. A positron emission tomography scan produces a three-dimensional image of the heart. p. 334

5. Three reasons have been suggested. First, physicians may be gender-biased in their delivery of health care and tend to concentrate on women's reproductive organs rather than on the whole woman. Second, physicians tend to view male heart disease as a more severe problem because medical training has traditionally focused on it as a "male" problem. Third, women decline major procedures more often than men do. p. 331

Practice Test 1

1. D, p. 319	6. D, p. 316	11. C, p. 325
2. D, p. 324	7. C, p. 319	12. A, p. 325
3. A, p. 325	8. A, p. 324	13. C, p. 334
4. B, p. 334	9. C, p. 318	14. A, p. 329
5. C, p. 324	10. C, p. 324	15. A, p. 324

Practice Test 2

1. A, p. 324	6. B, p. 318	11. D, p. 322
2. A, p. 325	7. C, p. 322	12. A, p. 324
3. D, p. 328	8. A, p. 329	13. D, p. 334
4. B, p. 329	9. C, p. 325	14. B, p. 334
5. A, p. 334	10. B, p. 329	15. C, p. 329

Chapter 13

General Review Questions

1. Cancer is the name given to a large group of diseases characterized by the uncontrolled growth and spread of abnormal cells. p. 341

2. People who engage in certain behaviors show a higher incidence of cancer. These behaviors include high-fat, low-fiber diet, sedentary lifestyle, consumption of alcohol and cigarettes, and high stress. p. 342

3. Risk factors for breast cancer include history of breast cancer, biopsy-confirmed atypical hyperplasia, long menstrual history, obesity after menopause, recent use of oral contraceptives, never having children, consuming two or more alcohol drinks per day, and higher education and socioeconomic status. p. 350

4. Benign tumors generally consist of ordinary-looking cells enclosed in a fibrous shell or capsule that prevents their spreading to other body areas. Malignant tumors usually are not enclosed in a protective capsule and can therefore spread to other organs. By the time they are diagnosed, malignant tumors have frequently metastasized throughout the body, which makes treatment extremely difficult. Unlike benign tumors, which merely expand to take over a given space, malignant cells invade surrounding tissue and emit clawlike protrusions that disturb the RNA and DNA within normal cells. p. 341

5. Asymmetry: one half of the mole does not match the other half; border irregularity: the edges are uneven, notched, or scalloped; color: pigmentation is not uniform; diameter: the diameter is greater than 6 millimeters. pp. 353–354

Practice Test 1

1. A, p. 342	6. D, p. 348	11. D, p. 341
2. B, p. 343	7. B, p. 348	12. B, p. 343
3. B, p. 342	8. A, p. 348	13. B, p. 354
4. B, p. 342	9. C, p. 348	14. A, p. 349
5. B, p. 343	10. D, p. 348	15. A, p. 350

Practice Test 2

1. D, p. 341	6. D, p. 348	11. B, p. 351
2. A, p. 342	7. C, p. 348	12. A, p. 353
3. A, p. 349	8. D, p. 348	13. C, p. 355
4. D, p. 350	9. D, p. 355	14. A, p. 341
5. C, p. 343	10. D, p. 350	15. C, p. 341

Chapter 14

General Review Questions

1. Your body uses a number of defense systems to keep pathogens from invading. The skin is the body's major protection, helped by enzymes. The immune system creates antibodies to destroy antigens. In addition, fever and pain play a role in defending the body. Vaccines bolster the body's immune system against specific diseases. p. 363

2. Acquired immunity refers to immunity developed during life in response to disease, vaccination, or exposure. Natural immunity is immunity passed to a fetus by its mother. p. 371

3. There are six major types of pathogens: bacteria, viruses, fungi, protozoa, parasitic worms, and prions. p. 365

4. Pathogens enter the body in several ways: direct contact between infected persons, or by indirect contact, such as through hands. You may also autoinnoculate yourself. Pathogens are also transmitted by airborne contact, food-borne infections, animal-borne pathogens, interspecies transmission, water-borne transmission, insect-borne transmission, and perinatal transmission. pp. 364–365

5. HIV typically enters one person's body when another person's infected body fluids gain entry through a breach on body defenses. pp. 383–384

Practice Test 1

1. C, p. 362
2. D, p. 365
3. B, p. 366
4. B, p. 395
5. C, p. 363
6. C, p. 389
7. B, p. 390
8. C, p. 371
9. B, p. 392
10. A, p. 396
11. C, p. 387
12. B, p. 393
13. C, p. 390
14. D, p. 384
15. D, p. 391

Practice Test 2

1. A, p. 378
2. C, p. 365
3. A, p. 368
4. D, p. 369
5. A, p. 369
6. A, p. 368
7. C, p. 394
8. B, p. 389
9. B, p. 387
10. B, p. 389
11. B, p. 391
12. B, p. 378
13. B, p. 390
14. C, p. 390
15. D, p. 394

Chapter 15

General Review Questions

1. Biological age, psychological age, social age, legal age, and functional age. pp. 400–401

2. They have managed to avoid serious diseases; they maintain a high level of physical functioning; they have maintained cognitive functioning; they are engaged in social activities; and they are able to cope with changes. p. 401

3. The five stages are denial, anger, bargaining, depression, and acceptance. pp. 409, 411

4. Active euthanasia refers to ending the life of a person who is suffering greatly and has no chance of recovery. Passive euthanasia refers to the intentional withholding of treatment that would prolong life. p. 414

5. The primary goals of hospice programs are to relieve the dying person's pain; offer emotional support to the dying person and loved ones; and restore a sense of control to the dying person, family, and friends. p. 415

Practice Test 1

1. A, p. 403
2. D, p. 401
3. D, p. 404
4. A, p. 405
5. B, pp. 401–402
6. B, p. 403
7. A, p. 404
8. B, p. 406
9. B, p. 406
10. C, p. 411
11. C, p. 406
12. B, p. 409
13. C, p. 412
14. C, p. 412
15. A, p. 415

Practice Test 2

1. B, p. 401		6. A, p. 409		11. A, p. 413	
2. A, p. 401		7. C, p. 402		12. C, p. 403	
3. C, p. 403		8. C, p. 412		13. D, p. 416	
4. B, p. 404		9. D, p. 403		14. B, p. 416	
5. C, p. 414		10. A, p. 412		15. C, p. 414	

Chapter 16

General Review Questions

1. Chlorofluorocarbon molecules are released from air conditioners, refrigerators, and the like. In the upper atmosphere, ultraviolet light breaks off a chlorine atom from a chlorofluorocarbon molecule. The chlorine atom attacks an ozone molecule and breaks it apart. An oxygen molecule and a molecule of chlorine monoxide are formed. A free oxygen molecule breaks up the chlorine monoxide. The chlorine is free to repeat the process. p. 427

2. Point source pollutants and nonpoint source pollutants are two general sources of water pollution. p. 429

3. The most widespread air pollutants that seriously affect health include sulfur dioxide, particulates, carbon monoxide, nitrogen dioxide, ozone, and lead. p. 422

4. PCBs were used as insulation in transformers. They are now found in landfills and waterways. They are associated with birth defects and cancer. Dioxins are chlorinated hydrocarbons found in herbicides. Long-term effects include possible damage to the immune system and increased risk of cancer. Pesticides are chemicals designed to kill insects. They end up in our water supply and in the land. They also cling to fruits and vegetables. Potential hazards include birth defects, cancer, liver and kidney damage, and nervous system disorders. Lead standards for drinking water have been strengthened. The use of leaded paints has been reduced in recent years. p. 429

5. Proponents believe nuclear power plants are a safe and efficient source of inexpensive electricity. Reliance on nuclear power can slow global warning. Overall, nuclear power plants account for less than 1 percent of the total radiation we are exposed to annually. Opponents charge that disposal of nuclear waste is difficult. They also cite concerns about the safety of nuclear power plants. Two serious accidents in the past have demonstrated the dangers involved with nuclear power. p. 435

Practice Test 1

1. A, p. 429		6. B, p. 424		11. A, p. 423	
2. B, p. 420		7. A, p. 425		12. A, p. 433	
3. C, p. 421		8. D, p. 427		13. D, p. 433	
4. A, p. 421		9. D, p. 428		14. C, p. 423	
5. C, p. 424		10. B, p. 422		15. A, p. 425	

Practice Test 2

1. D, p. 423	6. C, p. 432	11. D, p. 425
2. B, p. 431	7. B, p. 433	12. B, p. 426
3. B, p. 427	8. B, p. 424	13. C, p. 430
4. B, p. 428	9. C, p. 425	14. A, p. 432
5. D, p. 429	10. D, p. 425	15. A, p. 435

Chapter 17

General Review Questions

1. Self-care is the idea that the patient is the primary health care provider. Common forms of self-care include diagnosing symptoms of minor conditions; performing breast and testicular self-exams; learning first aid; checking your own blood pressure; and using home pregnancy test kits. p. 442

2. Three types of managed care plans include HMOs, point of service (POS) plans, and preferred provider organizations (PPOs). p. 451

3. Group practices involve physicians sharing offices, equipment and staff. They may also share profits. Solo practices involve single practitioners. There are far fewer of these today than in the past. p. 446

4. Medicare is a federal health insurance program for the elderly and the permanently disabled. Medicaid is a federal-state health insurance program for the poor. p. 450

5. A managed care system has a) a budget based on an estimate of the annual cost of delivering health care for a given population; b) a network of physicians, hospitals, and other providers linked contractually to deliver health care benefits within that budget and sharing the risk for any budget deficit; and c) an established set of rules requiring patients to follow the advice of participating health care providers in order to have their health care paid for under the terms of the health plan. p. 450–451

Practice Test 1

1. C, p. 440	6. A, p. 446	11. A, p. 445
2. C, p. 444	7. B, p. 446	12. D, p. 451
3. A, p. 445	8. D, p. 445	13. A, p. 446
4. B, p. 445	9. B, p. 440	14. B, p. 446
5. B, p. 446	10. C, p. 450	15. B, p. 450

Practice Test 2

1. A, p. 444	6. A, p. 450	11. D, p. 448
2. B, p. 441	7. D, p. 450	12. A, p. 450
3. A, p. 446	8. B, p. 441	13. A, p. 451
4. B, p. 451	9. C, p. 450	14. B, p. 446
5. D, p. 9	10. D, p. 451	15. B, p. 451

Chapter 18

General Review Questions

1. Complementary medicine is used with conventional medicine as part of the modern integrative medical approach. Alternative medicine is treatment used in place of conventional medicine. p. 456

2. Homeopathic medicine is based on the principle that "like cures like," meaning that the same substance that in large doses produces the symptoms of an illness will in very small doses cure the illness. Homeopathic physicians use herbal medicines, minerals, and chemicals. Naturopathic medicine views disease as a manifestation of an alteration in the processes by which the body naturally heals itself. Treatments include diet and nutrition, acupuncture, and herbal medicine. p. 458

3. Chiropractic medicine is based on the idea that a life-giving energy flows through the spine via the nervous system. Chiropractors manipulate the spine back into proper alignment. Osteopathic practitioners specialize in body manipulation yet also have a more traditional medical school training. Energy therapies focus on energy fields originating with the body or on fields from other sources. Acupuncture is one of the more popular forms of Chinese medicine among Americans. p. 459

4. Examples include qi gong, Reiki, and therapeutic touch. p. 459

5. Consult only reliable sources; remember that "natural" does not necessarily mean "safe"; recognize that alternative treatments are not closely regulated; recognize that dosage levels in herbal products are not regulated; talk to your doctor about herbal medicines; remember that herbal medicines are not miracle cures; and always look for the word "standardized" on herbal products you buy. p. 469

Practice Test 1

1. C, p. 457	6. D, p. 459	11. D, p. 459
2. A, p. 458	7. C, p. 459	12. C, p. 459
3. C, p. 458	8. A, p. 459	13. A, p. 459
4. B, p. 458	9. D, p. 466	14. C, p. 468
5. B, p. 458	10. D, p. 466	15. C, p. 459

Practice Test 2

1. C, p. 458	6. A, p. 465	11. D, p. 459
2. B, p. 458	7. D, p. 462	12. C, p. 458
3. A, p. 461	8. B, p. 461	13. B, p. 458
4. D, p. 465	9. C, p. 457	14. B, p. 460
5. B, p. 466	10. C, p. 460	15. A, p. 458